SOME FAMOUS STARS

By the same author

The Origin of the Earth
Foundations of Astronomy
Spherical Astronomy
Stellar Dynamics
The Sun, the Stars and the Universe
Astrophysics
Astronomy
Sea and Air Navigation (Halley Lecture)
Introduction to Sea and Air Navigation
Astronomical Navigation
Handbook of Sea Navigation

Also joint-author of

Admiralty Manual of Navigation (1922), Vols. 1, 2
Position Line Tables

Spiral Nebula seen edgewise
(*Mt. Wilson Observatory*)

SOME FAMOUS STARS

by

W. M. SMART
M.A., D.Sc.
President of the Royal Astronomical Society 1949–1951
Regius Professor of Astronomy in the University of Glasgow

LONGMANS, GREEN AND CO
LONDON ♦ NEW YORK ♦ TORONTO

MGE

LONGMANS, GREEN AND CO LTD
6 & 7 CLIFFORD STREET LONDON W I
ALSO AT MELBOURNE AND CAPE TOWN

LONGMANS, GREEN AND CO INC
55 FIFTH AVENUE NEW YORK 3

LONGMANS, GREEN AND CO
215 VICTORIA STREET TORONTO I

ORIENT LONGMANS LTD
BOMBAY CALCUTTA MADRAS

First Published 1950

PRINTED IN GREAT BRITAIN BY ROBERT MACLEHOSE AND CO. LTD.
THE UNIVERSITY PRESS, GLASGOW

PREFACE

The book is substantially a record of a course of eight lectures on "Some Famous Stars", delivered in the early months of 1949 in the Royal Technical College, Glasgow, on the David Elder Foundation.

Except for the Introductory Chapter which deals with several fundamental topics, the book is not of the systematic kind. In each of the subsequent chapters my object has been to focus attention on a major problem of Astronomy, with the historical observations associated with a well-known star as background, and thereafter to describe subsequent developments arising from more general investigations.

I am greatly indebted to the Directors of the Cambridge, Mt. Wilson, Norman Lockyer, Union (Johannesburg) and Yerkes Observatories for permission to reproduce the photographs with which the book is illustrated.

I take this opportunity of expressing my thanks to the Governors and Director of the College, to the audience for their interest and attention, and to the publishers and printers for the technical excellence of their production.

W. M. S.

9 *May*, 1950

CONTENTS

PLATES

Chapter I

INTRODUCTION

Astronomy differs from the other sciences in one distinctive way. Consider first the chemist; he conducts his researches by *handling* the objects of his investigations; he finds out the constitution of the organic or inorganic substances in which he is interested in terms of the chemical elements (iron, hydrogen, chlorine and so on) and the way in which the atoms of these elements are arranged within the smallest entity of the substance concerned; he investigates the properties of these substances; he deduces the laws of chemical combination; he can build up new substances out of the elements, sometimes for destructive purposes, as in the case of the so-called high explosives, sometimes for the advantage of humanity as in the case of the sulphonamides which have so greatly reduced the dangers to patients suffering from pneumonia and kindred diseases.

Again, the physicist can study in his laboratory such subdivisions of his subject as heat, light, sound, electricity and magnetism; he can deduce, for example, the laws of electromagnetism from his experiments and his fundamental researches give birth to the technological advances we see in the vast electric generating plants, in radio and in television, to take only a few examples; he can probe the interior of the atom, play with electrons, protons and neutrons; in the exigencies of total war he can invent the atom bomb, the most destructive weapon ever placed in the hands of man; and he is now about to turn the immense energy hidden in the atom to industrial uses. The geologist, botanist and zoologist depend in like manner on handling the objects of their investigations and studying them in laboratories or in their native habitats. Of the natural sciences chemistry and physics are most clearly defined; experiment comes first and then the great generalisations—the laws of chemistry and physics—follow.

Astronomy is in a different situation. In a sense the astronomer's laboratory is the Universe itself, but it is a domain which is completely beyond the reach of all his senses save one—sight. So far no human being has been able to adventure more than about 15 miles above the surface of the Earth and although the optimists in the many active societies for promoting interplanetary travel may achieve their first success, perhaps in the comparatively near future, in journeying to the Moon, it must be supposed that, even if the hazards of the outward and return journeys are successfully overcome, the heroic travellers will be the last to suggest that the Universe has no more secrets to be revealed. But, if we leave out what are likely to be only parochial surveys, the exploration of the Universe is admittedly the function of the astronomer and he achieves his purpose through the only bond between him and the stars, namely, that of the light which they radiate so profusely in all directions ; it may be added that only an infinitesimal part of the light emitted by a particular heavenly body eventually enters his eye, or the telescope, after an unbelievably long journey through the voids of space. Astronomy is thus, primarily, an observational science and it is well to remember that the only bridge between the astronomer and the stars is the light they radiate.

At first sight this must seem a flimsy link hardly likely to furnish us with much in the way of information of what a star really is and what its activities are ; but within the last hundred years it has become almost a truism that within the apparently insignificant modicum of light from a star are enshrined the secrets of its physical and chemical constitution—and of other things as well ; moreover, in recent times, the light of the distant nebulae can yield information about the organisation and evolution of the Universe itself. Although the bodily activities of the astronomer are limited substantially to the surface of the Earth—a small cosmic body no more than 8000 miles in diameter circling round the Sun in a mighty orbit of 186 million miles in diameter—yet his eye can penetrate to the depths of space and his mind can grapple with the problems of the Universe itself, thanks basically to the rays of light which reach him from afar.

As our main theme is connected with the stars, it may seem advantageous here to mention briefly some of the details we know about the star nearest to us—and the star of the utmost importance to us—the Sun. Our luminary is a vast globe of gas, about 865,000 miles in diameter and about 93 millions of miles from the Earth. It is extremely hot; in its outer gaseous layers the temperature is about 6000° C., a temperature never exceeded * as a result of human agency until the first atomic bomb exploded when, it is estimated, a temperature of several million degrees was attained. The temperature of the solar globe increases with depth below the surface and at the centre the temperature, derived from theoretical considerations, is about 20 million degrees. Such a hot body radiates vast amounts of heat and light energy, a minute portion of which falls upon the Earth and—considerations of austerity apart—makes life reasonably tolerable on our planet.

It must not be supposed that the Sun is very much like a white-hot cannon-ball; as we have stated, it is gaseous and just as there are atmospheric disturbances in our Earth's envelope of air—storms, tornadoes and so on—so in the Sun there are somewhat similar disturbances but, as can be imagined, on a much more extensive scale. At times, vast quantities of gas are thrown up from the solar surface, occasionally to heights of nearly a quarter of a million miles with speeds of scores of miles per second; these eruptions are known as "prominences", an example of which is shown in Plate I, facing page 32. It is not too much to suggest that many—if not all—of the stars in the heavens erupt in much the same way as the Sun; they are, in fact, not the placid, quiescent bodies they appear to be.

Just as the chemist can ascertain the chemical constitution of the terrestrial rocks, the oceans and the atmosphere so the astronomer can discover what elements are present in the Sun although the methods are, as a rule, different in the two cases; the chemist as we have suggested earlier can deal with an actual chunk of rock, boil it up with acids and apply his well-established chemical tests which finally lead him to recognise the presence of such and such chemical elements in his sample of

* The temperature resulting momentarily from the explosion of fine wires is an exception.

rock; the astronomer on the other hand has only the light from the Sun to investigate and it must strike the reader as a remarkable achievement that the constitution of our luminary can be inferred from what appears at first to be such scanty observational material as that furnished by sunlight. Indeed a hitherto unknown chemical element—the gas helium, second only to hydrogen in lightness—was first detected in the Sun at the total solar eclipse of 1868 and it was only in 1895 that the British chemist Sir William Ramsay discovered the gas in a mineral called cleveite and later—in minute proportions only—in the Earth's atmosphere. Towards the end of the first world war helium was found bubbling up from certain oil wells in considerable quantities, and because of its non-inflammable properties must surely have ousted hydrogen, as the medium of buoyancy, from the airship of the period if the controversy as to the relative merits of the airship and the aeroplane had not been settled indubitably in favour of the latter and thus rendered the former obsolete.

Such then is a brief description of the Sun. The stars as we shall see are suns at remote distances; some are many times larger, and others very much smaller, than the Sun but all are immensely hot gaseous globes radiating light and heat in much the same way as the Sun. No star has been recognised as a globe by direct observation in the telescope but this is hardly surprising when we become aware of the immense distances of the stars; at a distance of 93 millions of miles the diameter of the solar globe subtends an angle at the Earth of about half a degree; this is its *angular diameter*. This angle is about 270,000 times the angle which a solar diameter would subtend at the Earth if the Sun were as far away as the nearest star; such a minute angle cannot be detected by an observer using even the biggest telescope in the world in the ordinary way although by special optical devices the angular diameters of several giant stars can be and have been measured. The stars then are mere pin-points of light scattered over the dome of heaven and the main activities of astronomers until a century ago were mainly devoted to ascertaining first, their positions in the sky with ever-increasing accuracy and, second, their relative brightness.

More than two thousand years ago the ancient Greek astronomers subdivided the sky into *constellations*, the stars in a particular constellation suggesting perhaps the figure of one of their mythological heroes—for example, Hercules, Orion, Perseus and so on—perhaps the figure of an animal or bird—for example the Great Bear, the Eagle, the Swan and so on—and perhaps the names of familiar objects such as the Scales, the Northern Crown, etc.

The twelve constellations or " signs " of the *Zodiac* have even a longer history, for the sub-division of the narrow belt of the sky in which the Sun, Moon and the planets Mercury, Venus, Mars, Jupiter and Saturn—then known—are always to be found goes back forty centuries to Chaldean astronomy. In the earliest catalogue of stars, about a thousand in number, 48 constellations were recognised ; these covered only that part of the sky observable from Mediterranean latitudes. Nowadays, astronomers have subdivided the whole sky into 88 constellations, many of these in the northern sky following closely the boundaries assigned by the Greek astronomers.

The brightest stars bear Greek and Arabic names ; the former include such well known stars as Castor and Pollux and the latter include, for example, Vega (a corruption of " falling eagle "), Deneb (the " tail of the Swan "), Algol (a corruption of El Ghoul, " the Demon star ") and so on. It is said that at the conclusion of a lecture by a distinguished astronomer an old lady remarked to the lecturer that, although she had understood perfectly all he had been describing about the wonders of astronomy, she could not understand how he had contrived to know the names of the stars with which he appeared to be on such intimate terms. Such a naïve outlook is of course delightful but inconsistent with the recognition that it was the early astronomer's prerogative to name the stars in whatever way his imagination led him.

A systematic nomenclature was introduced by Bayer at the beginning of the seventeenth century ; the brightest star of a constellation was given the first letter Alpha of the Greek alphabet in association with the constellation concerned, the second brightest was given the second letter Beta, and so on ; thus we have Alpha Orionis (which also bears the Arabic name of Betelgeuse—the " shoulder of the giant ")—Beta Orionis with its Arabic name of Rigel,—the " foot of the giant ") and so on. On the exhaustion of the Greek letters, the Roman alphabet was pressed into service and we have stars named a Orionis, b Orionis, etc. When the telescope revealed immense numbers of fainter stars a further development in nomenclature became necessary and the first Astronomer Royal—the Rev. John Flamsteed—adopted the expedient of assigning numbers to the individual stars of a constellation ; thus we have stars named 1 Orionis, 2 Orionis, 3 Orionis, and so on. This method, of course, suffers from no limitations such as are inherent in Bayer's system and technically it could be applied to all the stars of a constellation revealed by the most powerful telescope. Actually, this method would become unwieldy in practice and instead, the fainter stars are usually identified either by the number assigned in a particular catalogue or by their positions in terms of what are analogous to terrestrial latitude and longitude or by the positions of their images on a photographic plate centred on a particular point of the sky.

We consider now the relative brightnesses of the stars. On a clear night we can see with the unaided eye perhaps two to three thousand stars ranging from Sirius (Alpha Canis Majoris)—the brightest star in the heavens—to the faintest star just perceptible to the eye. Estimates of brightness were first made in the second century B.C. by Hipparchus who assigned magnitude classes to the stars observed ; about a score of the brightest stars were designated " stars of the first magnitude ", the next fifty or so in brightness were considered to be of the second magnitude, and so until the sixth magnitude class was reached which referred to the faintest stars just visible on a clear night. The term " magnitude " in astronomy is in some ways unfortunate, as in normal usage it implies size or extent ; the reader, then, must not fail to remember that magnitude in the present connection signifies something associated with the relative brightness of the stars, and since we are comparing the brightness of the stars as we actually see them in the sky the magnitude concerned is more specifically referred to as *apparent magnitude*. Apparent magnitude is in some respects very much like a golf handicap ; the most efficient performers with handicaps not exceeding 6 are reckoned to be in the first class; the second class refers to the players with handicaps between 7 and 18, say; while the third class consists of the poorer performers with handicaps exceeding 18. Just as in golf the player with a particular handicap is reputed to be more efficient than a player with a larger handicap so, in astronomy, of two stars that one is the *brighter* to which is assigned the *smaller* magnitude number.

The relation between the brightness-ratio of two stars and the *difference* of their magnitude numbers is governed by a mathematical formula; for example, if one star is almost exactly $2\frac{1}{2}$ times brighter than a second the difference of magnitude is exactly 1·0; if the brightness-ratio is $2\frac{1}{2} \times 2\frac{1}{2}$, or $6\frac{1}{4}$, to 1 the difference of magnitudes is 2·0; if the brightness-ratio is 100 to 1, the difference of magnitudes is 5·0, and so on. Just as in golf the players of the second class have handicaps of 7, 8, . . . , 18 so stars of the second magnitude, for example, have magnitude numbers, derived from the formula alluded to, ranging from 2·0 to 3·0 usually in steps of a hundredth of a magnitude; thus the apparent magnitude assigned to a particular star may be expressed as 2·63. In deriving the magnitude of a particular star X the astronomer has to derive, by observation, the ratio of brightness of this star to the brightness of a standard star A; with suitable equipment he finds, for example, that A is $4\frac{1}{2}$ times brighter than X and, applying the formula, he calculates that the *difference* between the magnitudes of A and X is 1·63: since increasing magnitude numbers correspond to increasing faintness, the magnitude of X is *greater* by 1·63 than the magnitude of A: If the magnitude assigned arbitrarily to the standard star A is 1·0, then the magnitude of X is 1·0 + 1·63 or 2·63.

One or two stars have negative numbers expressing their apparent magnitudes. For example, suppose that a star S is $6\frac{1}{4}$ times brighter than our standard star A; by the formula this ratio of brightness corresponds to a magnitude-difference of 2·0; since the apparent magnitude of A is 1·0, the apparent magnitude of S is 1·0 *less* 2·0 or −1·0. Sirius, the brightest star in the sky, has the apparent magnitude of −1·58.

The reader may wonder why all this mathematical bother should be tolerated but when we reflect that the feeblest star, call it Y, visible in a particular telescope is so faint that our standard star A is found to be, say, 595,000 times brighter than Y, the method of using a magnitude-scale with its comparatively small range in numbers in preference to a brightness-scale with its enormous numerical ratios is seen to have its advantages ; in the case just quoted the brightness-ratio of 595,000 to 1 corresponds to a magnitude difference of 14·43 so that we can say that the star Y is of magnitude 15·43. With the new 200-inch telescope at Mt. Palomar in California stars as faint as the 20th magnitude can be *seen* and much fainter stars can be photographed. We shall later have to consider the astronomer's methods in deriving brightness-ratio ; meanwhile the reader can assume that the type of observation required furnishes the astronomer with satisfactory information about the relative brightness of the stars expressed in terms of apparent magnitude.

We now enquire into the reasons why a star A is $4\frac{1}{2}$ times brighter than a star X and 595,000 times brighter than a star Y. The first reason is that the stars are at widely differing distances from us ; just as in a street illuminated by arc-lamps of identical candle-power the nearest lamp appears the brightest, the second nearest appears to be the second brightest and so on, so in the same way if the stars were all of identical candle-power—or, if we like, exact copies of the Sun—then the nearest star will appear to be the brightest and the most distant the faintest.

A second reason arises from the fact that the stars are not all of the same size. Suppose that one of the two head-lamps of a motor-car is covered with black paper except for a central area of, say, an inch in diameter ; it is evident that the undimmed lamp sends out much more light than the other. Further, with suitable equipment placed, say, a hundred yards in front of the car we should find, under ideal circumstances, that the ratio of brightness of the two lamps was equal to the ratio of the areas through which light was emitted. In the same way the ratio of the brightness of two stars at the same distance from us is, other things being equal—we specify these later—equal to the ratio of the areas of the surfaces of the two stars and is thus dependent on the *sizes* of the stars.

A third reason relates to the surface-temperatures of the stars for, as a red-hot poker is much more luminous than a similar one that is just of a dull red colour—the temperature of the former being much higher than the latter—so a hot star is much more luminous than a cooler one of the same size and at the same distance. Again, it has been found in recent years that the space between us and the stars is not *clear* ; in different directions in the sky there is a sort of fog of varying blanketing-power so that if we had two identical stars at the same distance from us but in different directions that star would appear the fainter if the " fog " in its direction was thicker than that in the direction of the other star. With all these diverse factors operating it is evident that the simple fact that our star A *appears* to be $4\frac{1}{2}$ times brighter than the star X tells us nothing definite about the relative distances of the two stars, their relative sizes and temperatures, and the relative absorbing-power of the interstellar " fogs " through which their light travels to reach us on the Earth. Some of the principal problems in astronomy are concerned with the study and disentanglement of these factors.

Another feature of the stars is recognisable on a clear night either with or without the aid of a telescope and that is the diversity of their colours. Some stars such as Betelgeuse and Antares are unmistakably red in colour, Capella is yellowish and stars such as Rigel are blue. Colour is an indication of temperature, as in the case of the poker ; accordingly, we infer that the surface-temperature increases as we pass from Betelgeuse to Capella and thence to Rigel. One of the achievements of modern astronomy is the assignment of a specific value of surface-temperature to the stars ; for Betelgeuse, for example, it is about 3500° C., for Capella it is about 5500° C., for the Sun it is about 6000° C., and for Rigel about 12,000° C.

The degree of " twinkling " of the stars is associated with colour. The phenomenon itself is produced by the irregularities and changes in the terrestrial atmosphere and the effect is more notable for blue stars than for yellow stars and, still more, for red stars. Further, the effect is greater when the star is near the horizon than when it is high up in the sky ; this is due to the greater thickness of atmosphere through which the light of the star has to pass when it is near the horizon.

The labours of the early astronomers, so far as the stars were concerned, were devoted to deriving positions of the stars in the sky with the crude instruments then in use ; their observations were collected together in catalogues—one of the earliest of which is that of Hipparchus and substantially preserved in Ptolemy's *Almagest* written three centuries later. It is said that Hipparchus, who on any standards must be accounted one of the great astronomers of all time, was impelled to compile his catalogue, containing the positions and magnitude-classes of over a thousand stars, as the result of the appearance in 134 B.C. of a " new star " or *nova*, as such a star is called. No doubt Hipparchus considered it a matter of prime scientific importance that if stars were likely to appear and disappear (as all novae eventually do after the explosions which render them, temporarily, perhaps among the brightest stars in the sky), then the labour of collecting all previous observations, making new ones and assembling all the information in the form of a catalogue should be undertaken for the benefit of contemporary and future astronomy.

The compiling of the catalogue led to one unexpected result —perhaps the most important of Hipparchus' many discoveries —namely, that the axis about which the Earth rotates is not fixed in direction with regard to the stars but has a conical motion very much resembling the motion of the axis of a spinning-top. At present the direction of the Earth's axis in the sky (defining the north celestial pole) is close to the brightest star in the constellation of the Lesser Bear—this star is called the *Pole-Star*—and year by year the north celestial pole moves against the background of the stars completing its motion in the sky in a period of about 26,000 years ; the phenomenon is called the " Precession of the Equinoxes " and its explanation had to await the genius of Newton eighteen centuries after its discovery.

The invention of the telescope in 1609 introduced a new era in observational astronomy and it was soon possible to determine the position of the stars with an accuracy unattainable with the crude instruments of earlier times. The discovery of the New World and the establishment of colonial empires in all quarters of the globe necessitated a great improvement in the rudimentary methods of navigation as then practised. One of the first requirements was the compilation of astronomical tables giving the accurate positions of the Sun, the Moon, and the brighter stars and to meet the needs of navigation in these respects the Royal Observatory at Greenwich was founded by Charles II in 1675, its cost being met out of the sale of defective gunpowder! As already stated, the first Astronomer Royal was the Rev. John Flamsteed whose observational zeal and ability did so much to attain the end in view.

Although the telescope had been invented by a Dutchman who used it only for terrestrial observations, the credit of its application to the celestial scene is entirely Galileo's. The latter had heard of this new device which had the property of bringing, apparently, distant objects nearer and he immediately re-invented the telescope and applied it to celestial observations. Then followed the richest harvest of astronomical discoveries in the history of the science. Pointing his telescope at the Moon, he saw the lunar surface covered with mountain ranges and what we now refer to as craters; the Moon then resembled the Earth in many respects and could no longer be regarded—as it, generally, was up to that time—as composed of some celestial material differing from that of which the Earth was formed. The Milky Way, that white milky girdle of the sky, was seen to be composed of innumerable stars apparently jumbled close together, confirming a speculation of Democritus twenty centuries later (see Plate II, facing p. 33). The planet Venus was observed in changing crescent form, undergoing phases in much the same way as the Moon; hitherto it had been supposed that Venus was a self-luminous body shining by its own light; now it was concluded that Venus was a dark body, like the Moon, reflecting light from the Sun and so becoming visible.

Galileo's discovery of the four great Moons of Jupiter—eleven are now known—showed that the solar system was a much more complex organisation than was supposed up to that time, and the observation of sun-spots, coming and going in an apparently irregular manner, disposed of the Aristotelian conception of the immaculateness and unchangeability of the celestial bodies. Nearly a century before, Copernicus had advanced what was regarded at that time as a peculiar doctrine namely the theory that the Sun—and not the Earth—was the true centre of the world and that the Earth was merely a planet like Venus and Jupiter circulating around the Sun. The Copernican view found little favour at first—it was denounced by Luther and the Reformers as being contrary to Scripture and it was regarded as a suitable subject for what we should now describe as " music-hall buffoonery ". The discoveries of Galileo paved the way, in due course, for the general acceptance of the Copernican theory to which, in its broad outlines, nearly every subsequent astronomical discovery has contributed additional confirmation.

The astronomer's principal instrument is the telescope and it is convenient here to mention briefly just why it is such an important aid in observation. To the unaided eye the brightness of an object depends on the amount of light which passes through the clear aperture of the eye to the sensitive retina beyond ; this aperture is about one-fifth of an inch in diameter. If the diameter of the aperture were doubled, the area of the aperture would be four times greater ; accordingly, four times the amount of light would penetrate to the retina and an object would then appear four times brighter. We cannot of course modify the structure of the human eye but we can achieve an increase in the amount of light entering the eye by means of the optical device represented by the telescope.

In its simplest form the early telescope consisted of two lenses A and B supported in a tube or tubes (see Fig. 1) closed so as to keep out extraneous light. The lens A is called the *object glass* and on it falls a parallel beam of rays from a star, say. The refracting properties of the lens ensure that the parallel beam converges to a focus at F, beyond which it spreads out in a conical beam. The smaller lens B (called the eye-lens or eyepiece) is placed at such a distance from F that the light-rays falling on B are converted into a parallel beam which then enters the eye as shown. Such a telescope is called a refracting telescope or, simply, a refractor. Thus, if the diameter of A is ten times that of the clear aperture of the eye, the area of the cross-section of the parallel beam falling on A will be 100 times the area of the cross-section of the beam entering the unaided eye ; consequently, 100 times more light enters the eye than when the star is seen without telescopic aid ; in other words the star appears 100 times brighter in the telescope than when it is seen with the unaided eye. In this way, stars invisible to the unaided eye can be seen in the telescope. It is evident that if we want to see still fainter stars we must increase the size of the object-glass. There are practical difficulties which limit the size of object-glasses and the largest object-glass mounted in a telescope is the lens of 40 inches diameter of the Yerkes Observatory at Williams Bay, Wisconsin ; its *focal length*—that is the distance between F and the centre of A in Fig. 1—is 64 feet.

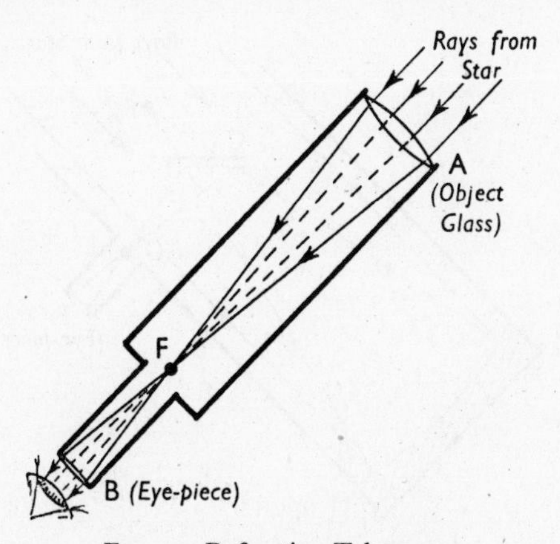

Fig. 1.—Refracting Telescope

A second property of a telescope relates to *magnification* which is defined to be the ratio of the focal length of the lens A to the focal length of the lens B (the focal length of B is the distance of F from the centre of B). The bigger the magnification the bigger the Moon, for example, will seem to be in the telescope ; accordingly its surface features can be studied in greater detail. Also, many stars which to the unaided eye appear to be single are actually double, consisting of two stars close together ; the bigger the magnification the further apart the two *components* (as they are called) will seem to be. To increase magnification it is necessary to substitute an eye-piece with smaller focal length. So far we have been discussing the original type of telescope with a pair of simple lenses acting as object glass and eye-piece respectively. For various reasons into which we need not enter the object glass and eye-piece of the astronomical telescope are compound lenses, but the general principles we have just been discussing are not altered in any significant way.

Most of the observational work today is photographic ; the photographic refractor consists of an object-glass mounted at the end of a tube, and at the focus F (see Fig. 1) a plate-holder is fitted ; there is of course no eye-piece as in Fig. 1.

The second type of telescope is the reflector which owes its light-gathering power to a mirror M (Fig. 2). The parallel rays from a star fall on the mirror and after reflection come to a

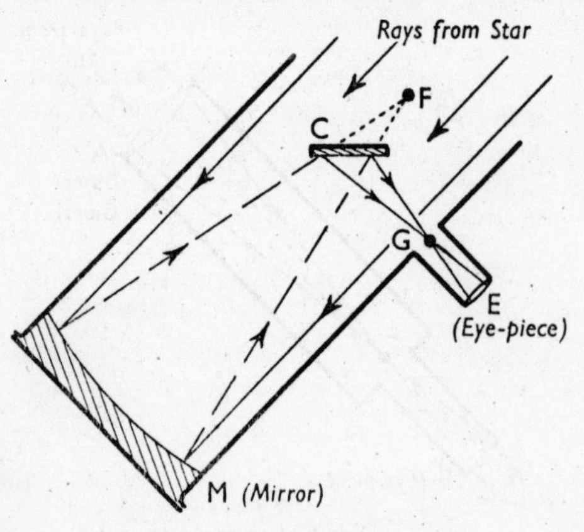

FIG. 2.—Reflecting Telescope

focus at F. It would obviously be inconvenient to have the eye-piece just beyond F, for the observer's head and shoulders would get in the way of the beam of light from the star, and so a small flat mirror is mounted at C which reflects the light to the side of the tube (or open strut-cage, as it usually is); the focus is at G and the eye-piece is at E. When the telescope is used for photographic purposes the eye-piece E is removed and a plate-holder is mounted at G. The reflector in the form indicated was invented by Newton, his first instrument being one of the cherished possessions of the Royal Society. The other form in which a reflector can be used is the Cassegrain, so-called after its inventor ; in this case the small mirror C is replaced by a small hyperbolic mirror so placed that it reflects the light back towards the main mirror M ; a small circular hole in M allows the light to come to a focus on the underside of M where it can be examined with an eye-piece or allowed to fall on a photographic plate.

The practical difficulties in making large mirrors with the requisite optical perfection, although great, are not insurmountable. The largest reflector (the Hale telescope) with a mirror-diameter of 200 inches is now in operation on Mt. Palomar in California, a giant compared with Newton's telescope of which the mirror-diameter was only one inch. The relative light-gathering power of the two instruments is in the ratio of 200×200 to 1—or 40,000 to 1—representing a magnitude-difference of $11\frac{1}{2}$; thus if Newton's instrument just allowed him to see a star of magnitude 10, the Californian giant will enable the observer to see a star of magnitude $21\frac{1}{2}$.

From the time of Flamsteed right up nearly to the end of last century a very large proportion of the work of practical astronomers was concerned with the measurement of star-positions ; most of the brightest stars in the sky—brighter, say, than the sixth magnitude—must have been observed scores or even hundreds of times in this way, with the result that their positions are now known with almost incredible accuracy, equivalent to the specification of a place on the earth's surface in terms of latitude and longitude with a possible error of only a foot or two. The star-positions so obtained are enshrined in the great catalogues published at intervals by the principal observatories. Amongst these may be mentioned one of the most useful—Argelander's Bonn Catalogue, published not quite a century ago, with the positions of 324,189 stars in the northern sky (including a very small zone of the southern sky) as faint as the tenth magnitude approximately. In addition to the catalogue, star-charts, based on the catalogue and covering the northern sky, were published and these are of very great value to the practical astronomer.

The observation of a single star for position is a somewhat tedious operation and for a particular instrument there is a limit in faintness beyond which it is impracticable to go. So by the middle of last century the practical astronomer saw little prospect of anything but an endless repetition of routine observations with, no doubt, improved equipment of the traditional kind. He was rescued from this unexciting life by two developments, first, the use of photography in astronomy and, second, (depending essentially on the first) the rise of a new branch of his subject, astrophysics.

The beginnings of photography in astronomy can be traced to 1850 when Whipple of Harvard Observatory succeeded in recording the images of Castor and Vega on the first type of photographic plate in use (the so-called " wet " or collodion plate). Seven years later G. P. Bond, also of Harvard, photographed the double star Zeta Ursae Majoris and deduced the angular separation of the two components and the direction in which the fainter component lay with respect to the brighter. But the " wet " plate by itself would not have seriously revolutionised astronomical methods and it was only in 1871 when gelatine was substituted for collodion and the " dry " plate brought into use that real progress could be made. Even then the full possibilities had not been appreciated although in 1876 Sir William Huggins—one of the great pioneers of astrophysics—had used the new plates successfully to photograph the spectra of several bright stars. With the invention of the dry plate a new industry was born with ever-increasing applications in all departments of science, technology and the ordinary affairs of life. It is surprising, however, that astronomers as a whole were so slow in perceiving that a new and powerful technique had just been placed at their disposal, and it was almost by accident that they woke up to realisation of the potentialities of the new methods.

In 1882 a bright comet was visible in the southern hemisphere ; at this time the ordinary photographic camera was the possession of a few enthusiasts of the new art and attempts were made to photograph the comet in the usual way. These attempts although of little direct scientific value convinced Sir David Gill, then H.M. Astronomer at the Cape of Good Hope Observatory, that the comet could be successfully photographed by a camera of this sort in combination with a telescope. With the slow plates of the period an " instantaneous " exposure was out of the question and so, enlisting the aid of an experienced photographer, Gill had the latter's camera strapped on the tube of a telescope, the driving apparatus of which ensured that as the comet moved across the sky from East to West—just as the Sun and stars move—the camera could remain trained on the object during an exposure of several minutes—or even longer. Several plates with exposures ranging from 30 minutes to 2 hours were secured. When the plates were developed satisfactory pictures of the comet were obtained, as Gill had hoped. But what astonished him was the fact that each plate showed clearly the images of hundreds of stars (see a similar photograph, that of Halley's Comet, in Plate III, facing p. 48).

Gill at once saw the immense potentialities of the photographic method for measuring the positions of even the faintest stars capable of recording their images on the plate. We have previously referred to the Bonn Catalogue containing the positions of about a third of a million of the northern stars, each position the result of one or more independent observations. At the time of the comet's appearance Gill was on the point of commencing a similar survey of the southern stars, obviously a gigantic enterprise involving many years of observations and calculations. The comet photographs disposed of this plan; instead, Gill determined to use photography to achieve his purpose, for which he acquired the necessary photographic equipment; beginning in 1885, he succeeded within the space of four years in covering the southern heavens *twice* and had the satisfaction of obtaining a permanent record of this portion of the sky at the time of the photographic exposures.

The business of deducing the positions of the stars from the stellar images on each plate had then to be undertaken. In 1878 Professor J. C. Kapteyn had been appointed to the Chair of Astronomy and Theoretical Mechanics at Groningen in Holland and, finding himself without instrumental equipment and with little prospect of acquiring any, he informed Gill that if the suggestion were agreeable to the latter, he would undertake the laborious job of superintending the measurement of the plates. As Gill had many preoccupations in other directions he eagerly accepted the offers of Kapteyn, thus inaugurating a fruitful collaboration with his eminent Dutch colleague that lasted long after the Cape Photographic Catalogue had been completed. It was fortunate for astronomy that Kapteyn, an enthusiastic and distinguished astronomer, lacked an observatory in which his great gifts might have been submerged in routine observations. Under his inspiration his university department at Gronigen became the " Groningen Astronomical Laboratory " where the most fruitful researches, based on the observational material of various observatories, have been successfully undertaken since Kapteyn's time up to the present day.

Meanwhile the brothers Henry of Paris had constructed a much more powerful photographic instrument than that with which Gill photographed the southern sky—the so-called astrographic telescope, of 13 inches aperture and 13 feet focal length. With this instrument stars as faint as the 15th and 16th magnitude could be readily photographed and to illustrate the power of the new method a single plate exposed on one region of the sky showed the images of nearly five thousand stars where only 170 had been observed (for position) by visual methods. On the suggestion of Gill an international conference—the first of its kind in any department of science—met at Paris in the spring of 1887 to explore the possibility of photographing the whole sky with instruments of the astrographic type. There was never any doubt amongst the delegates as to the outcome of the congress ; here was a fresh enterprise involving new and interesting techniques with problems of their own offering liberation from the dull routine of much contemporary work.

The main resolutions of the congress were two in number ; the first was to the effect that photographs showing images of stars as faint as the fourteenth magnitude should be secured and that reproductions—known now as astrographic charts—should be distributed to all astronomical institutions : the second involved the compilation of a catalogue with the positions and magnitudes of stars as faint as the eleventh magnitude. No less than eighteen observatories scattered over the northern and southern hemispheres signified their willingness to co-operate in the gigantic task and to each observatory was assigned a particular zone of the sky. To cover the sky twice over—a desirable extension of the original plan—it was necessary to secure about 22,000 photographs, that is, an average of about 1200 per observatory.

As soon as each observatory had acquired its own astrographic telescope the work began ; despite the initial enthusiasms, after sixty and more years, the project—as a whole—is still unfinished although several of the observatories have long since completed their share of the tasks allotted to them. There are several contributory reasons for this disappointing state of affairs ; it is pretty certain that few astronomers realised at the outset the magnitude of the task ; it is true that the actual photography of the sky was not exceptionally formidable when spread over two or three years—and actually most of this part of the project is complete—but the measurement of the stellar images on the plates and the necessary calculations for giving star positions imposed a very severe strain on any but the largest observatories ; it was difficult, too, for the staff of a small observatory to concentrate on a routine programme such as the astrographic chart when new and interesting problems of a wholly different kind cried out for investigation ; further, the expense of carrying out the programme—the printing of catalogues and the reproduction of charts were the chief items —was considerable and several observatories found great difficulty in obtaining the necessary funds from their national exchequers.

One of the objects of the project—which we have implied only casually—was the assignment of magnitudes to the stars of the catalogue. This involved, in the first instance, measuring the diameters of the images on the photographic plates ; now, a brighter star produces a larger image than a fainter star of *the same colour* and since blue light affects an ordinary photographic plate more than a red light, a blue star of equal *visual* brightness with a red star will produce a larger image than the latter ; and if we knew nothing about the colours of the two stars we should conclude from the measurements of the images on a plate that the former was brighter than the latter. It is evident then that the photographic scale of magnitude is different from the visual scale. The magnitudes deduced from the diameters of the stellar images are described as apparent photographic magnitudes and it is one of the tasks of the astronomer to investigate the relation between the visual and photographic magnitudes in terms of colour. We shall return later to this particular topic.

The reader may legitimately ask if all the labour associated with the production of the astrographic catalogue and chart was worth while. It is well to remember that the application of photography to astronomy was in its infancy at the birth of the project and, without some spectacular plan of the kind followed, the general adoption of photographic methods would, almost certainly, have been delayed considerably. Nor, perhaps, would the methods of relating the position of a star image on a plate to its position in the sky have been developed so rapidly, for this particular problem was forced on the attention of very many astronomers most of whom had their own contributions to offer. Perhaps an analogy will give some indication of the problem concerned. Suppose we have a map of, say, Yorkshire on the mercator projection lacking however the usual latitude and longitude scales ; suppose further that the latitude and longitude of one place, say York, is known ; the problem is to find out the latitude and longitude of every point marked in the chart. Knowing the nature of the projection our first task would be to construct latitude and longitude scales and no doubt we should draw the straight lines representing meridians and parallels of latitude at selected intervals on the chart. When all this is done, it is then easy to read off the latitude and longitude of any particular point on the chart.

The astronomer's task with a photographic plate is similar in character but very much more difficult in application ; the plate is of course a projection of part of the celestial sphere and the nature of this projection is known ; further, we may suppose for simplicity, that a star of known position has its image recorded at the centre of the plate and that two perpendicular lines parallel to the edges of the plate are drawn through the centre. Measurement of the plate consists in obtaining very accurately the distance of each star image from these central lines as indicated in Fig. 3, but the conversion of these distances in terms of the differences of the astronomical analogues of latitude and longitude has

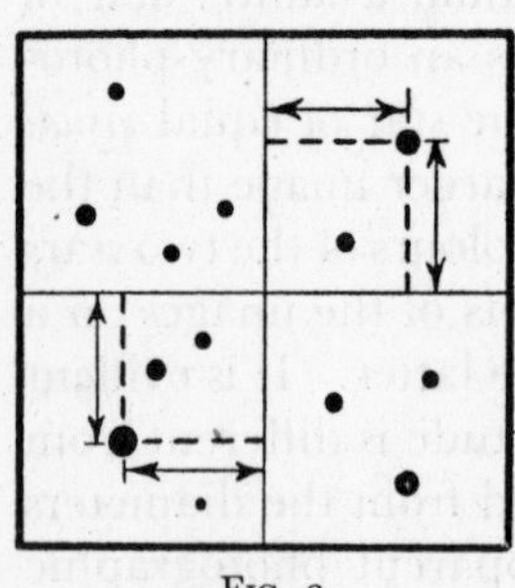

Fig. 3

to take account of several complications of which we refer to one only.

The light from a star does not come in a straight line from the star to the telescope for, in passing through the terrestrial atmosphere, its path is curved as the result of the optical phenomenon known as refraction ; the star is actually seen a little higher in the sky than it would be if the atmosphere were non-existent and this displacement in direction depends on the star's altitude—the nearer the star is to the horizon the greater is the displacement. Now, the stars photographed on a plate are not all at the same altitude and consequently the effect of refraction is to displace the star images by varying amounts. The measurements of a star's image from the two lines in Fig. 3 accordingly do not lead to the correct positions of the stars unless the effect of refraction can be removed from the measurements. When one reflects that there are several other causes operating in a similar sort of way to require the correction of the actual measurements in Fig. 3, the problem of deriving the true position of a star from plate-measurements is evidently one of considerable complexity. Fortunately, in actual practice, a simple method has been devised to take account, in a single operation, of *all* the disturbing factors and consequently the positions of the stars in the sky can be deduced from the plate-measurements with surprisingly little trouble.

Again, the counting of the numbers of stars of different magnitudes enabled astronomers to make a concerted attack on the distribution of the stars at much greater distances from the Sun than had yet been attempted in a systematic manner. The underlying assumption in such investigations was the simple one that increasing faintness of the stars is associated with increasing distance ; we have seen earlier that the apparent brightness of a star depends on additional factors but in the present instance, in which statistical methods were employed, the assumption had much to commend it. In any event a great deal was learned about the distribution of stars in our stellar system which has formed the basis of subsequent studies.

But the greatest use of the astrographic project is related to the fact that a detailed picture of the sky was recorded accurately at the time of the exposure of the plates. The significance of this can be appreciated only after we introduce a new concept. The stars are frequently referred to as "fixed" by which we are supposed to infer, for example, that the configurations of the constellations remain unaltered from century to century. We now know that this is not so. Instead of thinking of the stars as ships anchored all over the North Sea, for example, we must think of them as ships going about their lawful occasions each steaming at a constant speed on a constant course ; in other words the stars are rushing about in space with all sorts of speeds in all sorts of directions. The result is that the stars, say, in a small part of the sky appear to be changing their positions at different rates and in different directions ; accordingly the configuration of such stars will alter from year to year but the change is so small that it can be measured only from accurate observations made at the beginning and end of an interval of perhaps twenty years ; the procedure in the case of a particular star is fundamentally to determine its astronomical latitude and longitude say in 1940 and again in 1950 ; the observations allow us to find out the change of position of the star as viewed against the background of faint and practically immobile stars during this interval ; moreover, the greater the interval, the greater is this change in position ; the angular rate at which a star is changing its position in one year, in the sense indicated above, is called the *proper motion* of the star.

The study of proper motions has become, since the beginning of the century, a most important department of astronomical research with which we shall deal in greater detail in later chapters. Meanwhile it is sufficient to state that the early astrographic plates and similar plates taken two or three scores of years later enable us to measure the proper motions of the fainter stars all over the sky with very considerable exactitude and with the expenditure of comparatively little labour. Since the proper motions of the fainter stars are generally very small, the length of interval associated with their measurement is of prime importance and this is an advantage possessed by the astrographic project over all others. It is true that the improvement in the size and quality of photographic telescopes in recent years has tended largely to counterbalance this advantage, and for this reason—and others—the balance of expert opinion is against the completion of the astrographic plan in its original form. Except for future investigations of proper motions the astrographic chart has served its purpose and remains a worthy monument of collective enterprise.

Some of the advantages of photography over visual observations have already been implicitly suggested in the previous pages and it may be convenient here to summarise the more important. First of all a single photographic plate—the taking of which is a simple operation—shows the relative positions of the stars at the time of the exposure of the plate and remains a permanent record of the part of the sky concerned ; the mapping of all the stars by the older visual observation methods would be a lengthy and wearisome operation. Further, the photographic magnitudes of the stars can be quickly measured. In the next chapter we shall be concerned with the problem of measuring a star's distance ; it is true to say that little progress would have been made by visual observations alone and it was only on the supplanting of these by the much more accurate photographic method that our knowledge of stellar distances was so immensely increased. Again, the photographic telescope has an immeasurable advantage over the eye as an observing instrument ; the eye records only the instantaneous impressions of the light which falls on the retina ; the photographic plate during an exposure of several minutes, for example, adds up—so to speak—these instantaneous impressions and records the sum-total on the plate ; the consequence is that by increasing the length of the exposure we can obtain the images of fainter and yet fainter stars (or of objects such as the very distant nebulae), the faintest of which have never been *seen* by the human eye implemented as it is by the most powerful telescope. As he proceeds through the following pages the reader will easily recognise for himself the vast accession of power in many fields which photography has placed in the hands of astronomers.

We began this chapter by referring to light as the only bridge between the astronomer and the stars ; so far we have been mainly concerned with two features of the light from a star—the amount which reaches us and the direction in which it comes. We have however mentioned colour and that brings us to the physical properties of light. It was Sir Isaac Newton who first demonstrated the composition of sunlight by passing a narrow beam of light through a glass prism and showing that sunlight was a mixture of the colours which we see in the rainbow—red, orange, yellow, green, blue and violet ; further, by the use of a second prism he reunited the coloured beams into white light. The prism produces what is called a *spectrum* and the rainbow is merely Nature's spectrum produced not by a prism but by the spherical water-globules in the Earth's atmosphere.

Light, then, has inherent qualities and properties the study of which has enabled us to acquire a knowledge of the physical constitution—and movements—of the heavenly bodies to an extent that would have seemed incredible to astronomers a century ago. The breaking-up of light by a prism into its constituent colours is the foundation on which the vast edifice of astrophysics has been reared and, it may be added, in this branch, too, photography has played a notable part. As the name implies, astrophysics is the application of physical principles to the investigation of the heavenly bodies ; it is here that the astronomer is particularly dependent on the physicist to supply the interpretation of the various phenomena which he meets in astronomical spectroscopy which may be briefly described as the study of the spectra of the stars and the other heavenly bodies.

Chapter II

61 CYGNI

THE FIRST MEASUREMENT OF THE DISTANCE OF A STAR

In this chapter we shall be concerned with one of the greatest achievements of last century, the first successful attempt to measure the distance of a star. This was the first stage in the real appreciation of the immensity of the stellar universe.

From earliest times man must have speculated on this particular problem of the distances of the stars. The principal observable phenomenon of the heavens was the daily motion of the Sun, Moon, planets and stars across the sky, from their rising in the East to their setting in the West—the diurnal motion, as it is called. The Earth *seemed* to be fixed and immovable in the centre of the Universe and if this were granted it was an easy step to suggest that the stars were objects on a glass-like sphere which was imagined to revolve around the central Earth at a uniform rate. This was the Aristotelian conception of the stellar system, a conception which dominated European thought for nearly a score of centuries. As we have mentioned in the preceding chapter, the geocentric theory was eventually supplanted by the simpler hypothesis of Copernicus—the heliocentric theory—that the Sun was the true centre of the system of planets and that the Earth was merely a planet, like the others, circulating around the Sun ; moreover, the diurnal motion was easily explained on the supposition that the Earth rotated at a uniform rate about an axis in the period of a day—more accurately, 23 hours 56 minutes of mean solar time. On this latter hypothesis there was no need any longer to suppose that the stars were all fixed on a glass-like sphere ; instead they could be regarded as being situated at immense and at varying distances in space, immobile like ships at anchor, the apparent constancy of the configurations of the constellations lending support to this idea.

As we have seen, many of the objections to the Copernican doctrine gradually disappeared with the discovery of new phenomena; but one objection refused stubbornly to be disposed of. If the Earth, according to Copernicus, moved in a mighty orbit (which we know today to be 186 million miles in diameter) and if the stars were at different distances from us, then two stars close together in the sky, one being farther away in space than the other, would appear to be closer together say in March than they would be six months later when the Earth was 186 million miles away from its position in March. This can be illustrated by a very simple experiment which the reader is earnestly invited to perform. Hold up a finger (F in Fig. 4), at arm's length roughly in the direction of a more distant object, O, such as a book on a shelf or a lamp a few yards away or a church spire. With the right eye closed, the direction of the finger as seen by the left eye, L, is, we shall suppose, in the direction LA, close to the direction of the object O. Now, without moving the head, close the left eye and open the right. The direction of F as seen by the right eye, R, is then indicated by RB; F is now seen to be much farther to the left of O than when it was viewed by the left eye. Think now of O as a very distant star and F as another star much nearer to us than O; if L represents the Earth's position in space say in March and R its position six months later, then our experiment would seem to show that the star F has altered its position in the sky relative to the star O in the course of six months, being farther away from O, as regards direction, in September than in March.

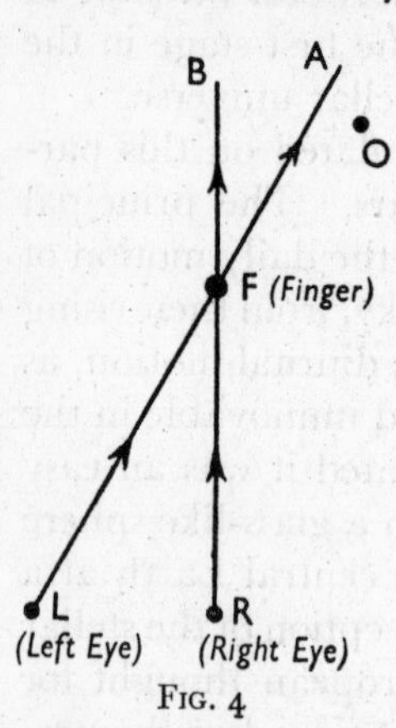

FIG. 4

This principle was early understood but, as the comparatively crude observations of the stars in Copernican and later times revealed no changes of the expected kind, the objection to the planetary character of the Earth as a body changing its position, with respect to the Sun, in its yearly motion around our luminary remained a stumbling block unless it were conceded that the stars were so far away that the changes in the direction of a star such as F with respect to a more distant star O (Fig. 4) were too small to be detected by the instruments of the time.

The method of utilising a faint and presumably distant star, as illustrated in Fig. 4, for measuring the change in direction of a near star corresponding to different positions of the Earth in its orbit was specifically mentioned by Galileo in his famous book, *Dialogue of the two chief systems* (*Ptolemaic and Copernican*), published in the early years of the seventeenth century. As the Copernican ideas became more firmly established, so it became certain that the stars must be at immense distances from us and that the problem of measuring the distance of even the nearest must depend on introducing a much more accurate observational technique than was available in the early days of tele-

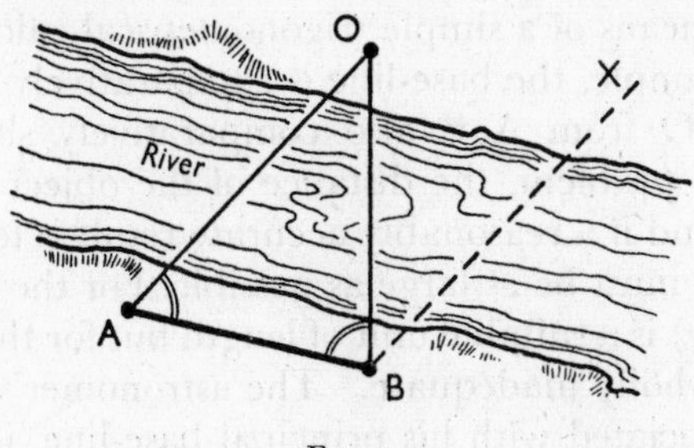

FIG. 5

scopic construction. The challenge thus thrown out to astronomers was not successfully met until 1838, roughly four centuries after the Copernican theory had indicated the chief features of the method to be employed.

To measure the distance of any inaccessible object we must have a base-line of known length. The method adopted by the land-surveyor in finding the distance of an object, say, on the far bank of a broad river is basically the method used by the astronomer in finding the distance of a star. Suppose that in Fig. 5 the distance of an object O from a point A is required. With a chain the surveyor measures out a base-line AB of say a hundred yards, sticking in a pole vertically at B. With a theodolite at A he measures the angle between AB and AO. After sticking a pole in the ground at A he carries his theodolite to B, erecting it over the point in the ground in which the pole at B had been placed, and then measuring the angle between BA and BO. As the three angles of a triangle (AOB) add up to 180°, he easily deduces the angle AOB which is easily seen, by drawing BX parallel to AO, to be the change of direction of O as viewed from A and from B.

He has now enough data to draw the triangle AOB to scale, say 100 yards to be represented by 1 inch ; he draws AB equal to 1 inch, sets out a line AO with a protractor so that the angle OAB is equal to his first theodolite measure and a line BO so that the angle ABO is equal to the second theodolite measure. These lines meet at O and the measurement of AO in inches leads to the distance of O from A in yards. In practice, this method of drawing a triangle to scale is really not as accurate as is generally desirable and accordingly the distance AO is derived by means of a simple trigonometrical calculation.

In this example, the base-line is comparatively short, for the distance of O from A is also comparatively short. In the astronomer's problem, the distance of the object O is exceedingly great and if a reasonably accurate result is to be obtained the base-line must be as large as possible. For the surveyor, the yard (or mile) is a suitable unit of length but for the astronomer this unit is wholly inadequate. The astronomer's chief unit of distance, associated with his principal base-line, is the average distance of the Earth from the Sun—that is, 93 million miles (half the diameter of the Earth's orbit, previously referred to) ; this is called the *astronomical unit of distance* and we shall now describe briefly how this unit has been obtained, adding the remark that the activities of many generations of astronomers, right up almost to the present day, have been devoted to deriving this unit with the utmost possible accuracy.

A first requirement is an accurate knowledge of the dimensions of the Earth. For our purpose it is sufficient to regard the Earth as a sphere whose radius we now know to be 3960 miles —we need deal only with round numbers. The measurement of the Earth's radius was first achieved by Eratosthenes in the third century B.C. The method is illustrated by means of Fig. 6, in which Alexandria and Syene * (two places in Egypt

* The site of the great dam on the Nile at Assouan, in modern geographical nomenclature.

nearly on the same meridian) are represented by A and B respectively ; C is the centre of the Earth. At midday at the time of the summer solstice (about June 21) the direction AS of the Sun (denoted by S) at Alexandria was found to be about 7° from the direction, CAD, of the point of the sky overhead at A ; this is another way of stating that the altitude of the Sun was 90° less 7°, or 83°. It was also known that at the time of the summer solstice, the Sun was exactly overhead at Syene at midday and therefore it must be on the continuation of the line joining C to B, as shown in Fig. 6 ; this fact, it is said, was

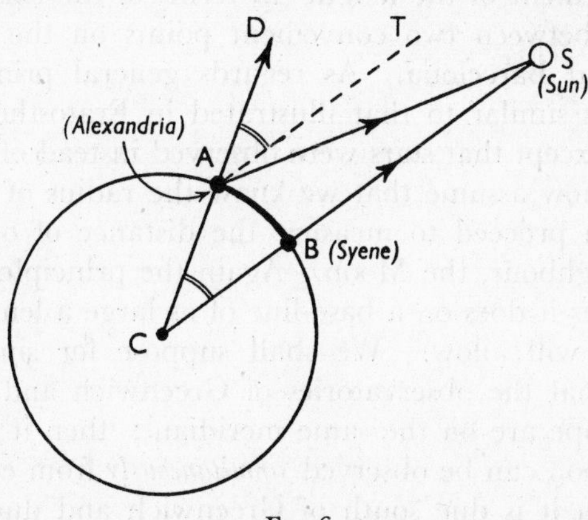

FIG. 6

deduced from the observation that the Sun's reflection was seen from the water-level of a deep well at Syene.

Eratosthenes made the assumption (which we now know to be justified) that the distance of the Sun from the Earth was exceedingly great in comparison with the Earth's radius ; this implied that the directions AS and CS were nearly parallel so that the angles DAS and ACS must be substantially equal ; in other words the angle ACB must be 7°, corresponding to about one-fiftieth of the circumference of the circle of which AB is a part. Now the length of the arc AB (the distance of Syene from Alexandria) was known ; hence the length of the circumference of the circle on which A and B lie is 50 times the length of the arc AB ; from this the radius of the Earth is easily deduced.

Of course this measurement of the radius of the Earth was fairly rough and later geodetic surveys have given much more accurate results. One of the most notable of these was undertaken in 1795 by French geodesists, in the first flush of revolutionary fervour to invent new standards with the object of putting science on a rational basis ; this survey gave birth to the unit of length called the *metre* used now almost exclusively in scientific work. It was designed to be one ten-millionth part of the distance from the equator to the North Pole along the meridian of Paris and the essential part of the scheme was the measurement of the length (in terms of the existing unit) of the arc between two convenient points on the meridian, Dunkirk and Barcelona. As regards general principles the method was similar to that illustrated in Eratosthenes' measurements except that stars were observed instead of the sun,

We can now assume that we know the radius of the Earth and we can proceed to measure the distance of our nearest celestial neighbour, the Moon. Again the principle is simple, depending as it does on a base-line of as large a length as circumstances will allow. We shall suppose for simplicity of argument that the observatories of Greenwich and the Cape of Good Hope are on the same meridian ; then it is possible that the Moon can be observed *simultaneously* from each observatory when it is due south of Greenwich and due north of the Cape Observatory.

The actual observation at Greenwich, for example, consists in measuring the angle between the direction of the Moon (a small crater near the centre of the Moon's disc is chosen for this purpose) and the overhead direction CGA at Greenwich (denoted by G in Fig. 7) ; the angle AGM is then known—we omit all considerations of instrumental and other corrections.

Similarly, the angle between the direction of the crater as viewed from the Cape (O in the figure) and the overhead direction, COB, is measured ; this is the angle BOM. Further, the angle GCO is known—it is the sum of the north latitude of Greenwich and the south latitude of the Cape Observatory—and since CG, CO are radii of the Earth the angles CGO and COG are equal and can then be found, for the angle GCO is known. Since the angles AGM and GCO are known we deduce the value of the angle MGO from the fact that CGA is a straight line. Similarly, we deduce the angle MOG. The base-line is GO which can be calculated from our knowledge of the angle GCO and the radius of the Earth.

The problem is then reduced to the surveyor's problem illustrated in Fig. 5 and we can calculate the length of GM ; a further step in calculation gives us the distance of the Moon from the Earth's centre—strictly, it is the distance of the crater, but a further step which we need not specify gives us the required distance of the Moon's centre at the time of observation. Our exposition has followed simple geometrical ideas and although the astronomer's method of reaching the desired

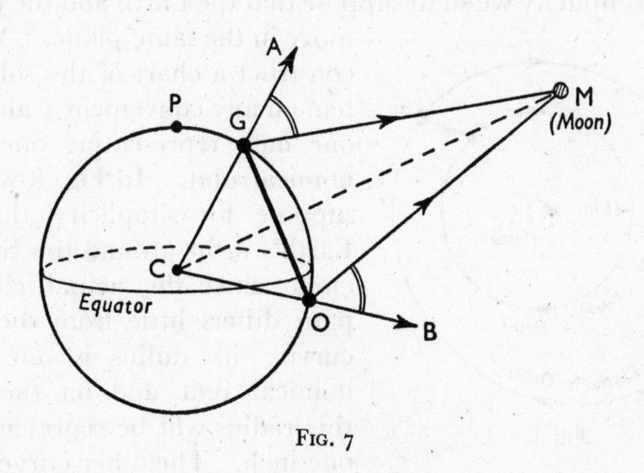

Fig. 7

result is more involved, nevertheless the underlying principles are essentially those illustrated in Fig. 7. It may be added that the Moon's average distance from the Earth is close to 240,000 miles ; further it moves around the Earth in an elliptical orbit, its maximum and minimum distances from the Earth being about 253,000 and 227,000 miles respectively.

The astronomer's yardstick is as we have said, the astronomical unit—the average distance of the Earth from the Sun. At first sight it might seem feasible to employ the same method for the Sun as in the case of the Moon. However, the Sun is not a solid body like the Moon and there is, of course, no permanent and sharp feature such as the lunar crater referred to earlier ; there are other serious disadvantages in the method which we need not specify. Accordingly, to obtain accurate results we have to set about the business in a different way. Now, it is easy to find the average distance of any planet from the Sun in terms of the astronomical unit by means of Kepler's laws, the first of which states that the path (or orbit) of any planet around the sun is an ellipse with the sun at one focus of the ellipse. The third law which is expressed in simple mathematical form enables us to calculate very easily the average distance of a planet from the Sun in astronomical units when its orbital period, in years, is known ; the latter is readily obtained from observations.

For simplicity we shall suppose that the Earth and the planets move in the same plane. We can construct a chart of the solar system on any convenient scale—say, one inch representing one astronomical unit. In Fig. 8 we shall suppose for simplicity that the Earth's orbit around the Sun is a circle, since the actual elliptical path differs little from the latter curve ; its radius is one astronomical unit and on the chart this radius will be represented by one inch. The other curve in the diagram represents the elliptical path of a planet such as Mars or Eros (the latter a minor planet discovered towards the end of last century). The feature of this particular orbit is that at certain times the Earth (denoted by E) and the planet (denoted by P) can be comparatively close together as in the configuration represented in Fig. 8 where the exact positions of E and P can be specified.

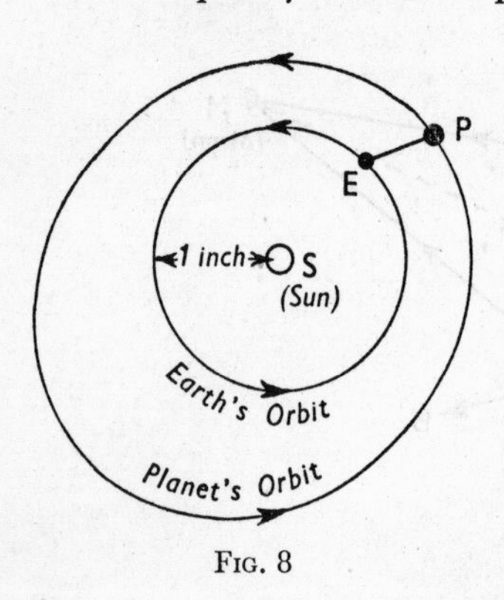

Fig. 8

On the chart we can measure the distance EP ; suppose it is $\frac{1}{4}$ inch which therefore represents $\frac{1}{4}$ astronomical unit. Further, as we shall see, we can measure the distance, represented by EP, in miles ; suppose it to be 23 million miles. We then conclude that $\frac{1}{4}$ of an astronomical unit is equal to 23 million miles and consequently one astronomical unit is equivalent to

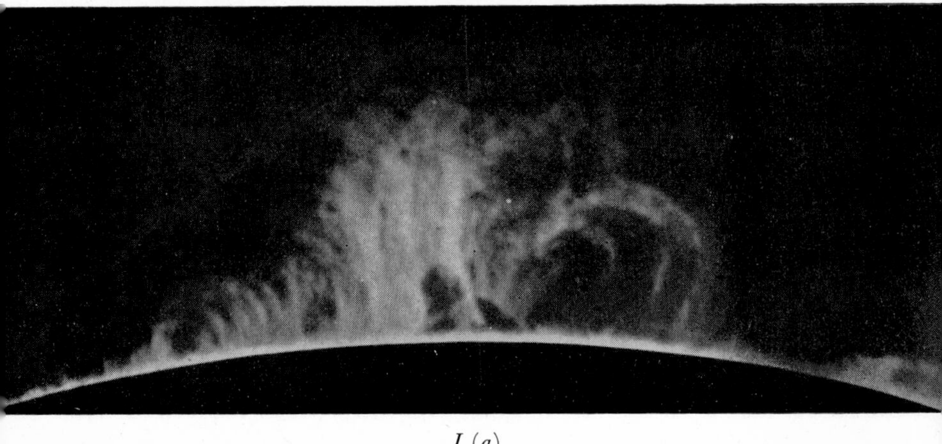

I (a)

I (b)

I(a) and (b) Photographs of a Solar Prominence

(Yerkes Observatory)

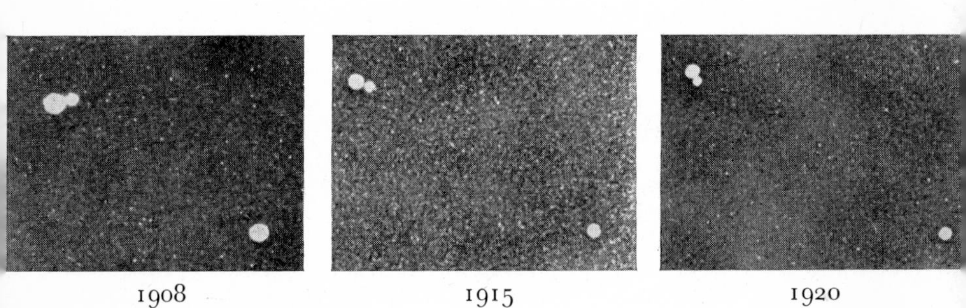

I(c). Three photographs of the binary Kr. 60 *(top left-hand corner) in* 1908, 1915 *and* 1920, *showing revolution of the fainter star about the brighter*

(Yerkes Observatory)

II. Two regions of the Milky Way
(Yerkes Observatory)

92 million miles which, otherwise expressed, is the Earth's distance from the Sun.

This then is the fundamental principle, and we select for observation a planet which can, under favourable circumstances, be at a comparatively small distance from the Earth, for then the unavoidable errors of observation, however small, will have the least effect on the measurement, in miles, of the distance between the two bodies. In the latter part of last century Mars and two minor planets were observed for the purpose under consideration, their orbits being elongated as depicted in Fig. 8, with not wholly satisfactory results. But in 1898, the discovery of Eros, which can come as close as 14 million miles to the Earth, and the application of photographic methods introduced elements of precision unattainable in previous investigations.

It is to be remembered that we must have a base-line of known length. When we described the method of measuring the Moon's distance the base line was defined by means of two observatories, Greenwich and the Cape, from which simultaneous observations of the Moon were made. This method has one obvious disadvantage when we are restricted to a period of observation of but two or three months, as in the case of Eros under the circumstances depicted in Fig. 8 ; this disadvantage, of course, is that many observations would be wasted owing to unfavourable weather conditions at one or other of the two observatories on the *same* days. But how can another base-line not depending on *two* observatories be obtained ? The solution is found in the fact that, taking only the simplest factor, a particular observatory is changing its position in space owing to the rotation of the Earth ; if the observatory is situated at the Equator, then in the course of 12 hours, its position will have changed as a result of rotation by a distance equal to the diameter of the Earth or 7920 miles ; for observatories not on the equator, the distance will be less, but even for the most northernly or southernly observatories this distance will exceed 4000 miles. This then is our base-line.

The proceedure for measuring the distance of Eros is to observe the planet when it is as far East in the sky as is practicable and then to repeat the observations when the planet is as far west in the sky as is practicable. Suppose these observations are made at 6 p.m. and 6 a.m. on the following day. We then obtain the position of the planet in the sky as viewed from the ends of the base-line appropriate to the observatory concerned. The geometrical problem is then fundamentally the problem of the surveyor.

As soon as the orbit of Eros had been determined after the planet's discovery in 1898 it was seen that unusually favourable circumstances for the measurement of the Sun's distance would occur in the winter of 1900-1901, and about a score of observatories undertook to make the requisite observations. Most of these were photographic observations made as follows. A plate taken say at 6 p.m. showed the position of Eros with respect to the background of the stars; this position is represented by E_1 in Fig. 9, the images of the stars being represented by the black dots. Twelve hours later—or after as convenient an interval as was practicable—a second photograph was taken in which the position of the planet against the background of the same stars was obtained. If we suppose this position to be inserted accurately on the first plate, it would be represented by some such point as E_2. The measurement of the plates gives in effect the change of direction of the planet as seen at the two times of observation.

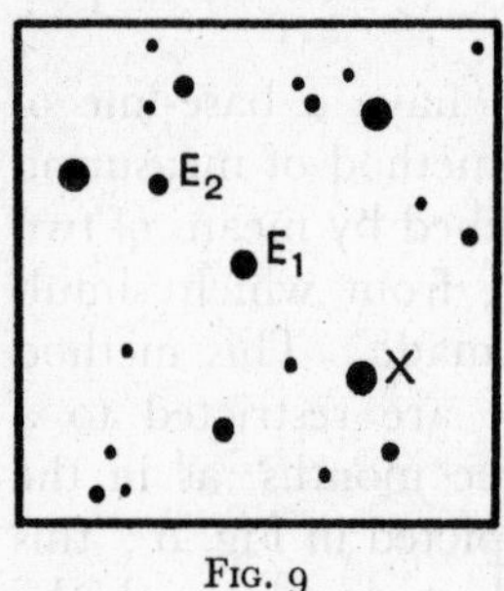

FIG. 9

Recurring to our eye and finger illustration, E_1 corresponds to the direction of our finger (representing Eros) in relation to a distant object—say, a church spire—representing a star X in the figure, when our observation is made with the left eye (representing one end of the base-line); and E_2 corresponds to the direction of our finger when the observation is made with the right eye (representing the other end of the base-line).

The superintendance of the 1900-1901 observations of Eros was undertaken by A. R. Hinks of Cambridge Observatory; the measurement of the plates and the necessarily elaborate discussion of these measures proved a long and difficult task and it was about ten years after the planet had been observed that

Hinks was able to announce the final result of this co-operative effort, namely, that the Earth's average distance from the Sun—that is, the astronomical unit—is 92,900,000 miles.

The next favourable occasion for observing Eros in this connection occurred about 30 years later and elaborate preparations were set on foot to secure still greater accuracy in the measurement of the astronomer's principal yard-stick—the astronomical unit. The work of the many observatories was under the general superintendance of the Astronomer Royal, Sir Harold Spencer Jones, and about ten years after the necessary observations had been made he announced that the second Eros campaign yielded the following:

1 astronomical unit = 93,003,000 miles,

a result that must be accorded a very high degree of accuracy.

It is sometimes asked if the expenditure of such tremendous efforts are justified when the most recent result appears to have improved the earlier measurement only by roughly one part in a thousand. The answer is that the astronomer does want to know with considerable accuracy what his yard-stick is equivalent to in miles, not because it is a desirable end in itself but because the astronomical unit enters into other problems and phenomena and sometimes in such a way that a somewhat inaccurate value of the unit might frustrate seriously the investigation of the problem or phenomenon concerned. However, even if Eros were in a suitable position for observation within the next ten or twenty years it is fairly certain that astronomers would rest content on the laurels already so hardly won.

We now approach the main core of this chapter—the measurement of a star's distance. As we have remarked earlier the principle of the method is inherent in the Copernican conception of the solar system, the requisite base-line being the diameter of the Earth's orbit around the Sun, which as we have just seen, is now known with very high accuracy. Many attempts were made to bridge the gulf between us and the stars and although all those were unsuccessful in their object until 1838 two, in particular, stood out because of the unexpected discoveries that resulted.

The first of these was the discovery of the phenomenon of

aberration by Bradley in 1728. Bradley, who later became Astronomer Royal (the third of the succession), embarked on a long series of observations in an attempt to measure the distance of the star Gamma Draconis (the third brightest star in the constellation of the Dragon). He chose this star, first, because it was bright, being of the second magnitude for, other things being equal, there was a distinct chance that it might be within measurable distance and, second, the star passed almost overhead at the observatory where he was making the observations, so that the somewhat uncertain effect of refraction by the Earth's atmosphere could be disregarded.

His investigation was made with a telescope which was kept in a fixed vertical position throughout the long series of observations and, without going into details, these observations furnished him with the star's position in the sky at the time of each observation. Now, if the star were so near that its changes in direction throughout the year were unmistakable then the nature of his observations—which we need not particularise—would have been sufficient to give him the information required, namely, the star's distance. Instead, he found that the variation in the star's observed positions throughout the year was completely incompatible with the kind of variation anticipated. He had evidently stumbled across a new phenomenon, the interpretation of which added new confirmation to the Copernican theory that the Earth was a planet circulating around the Sun.

A Danish astronomer had proved some years previously that light does not come to us through space instantaneously but that it has a finite velocity which he estimated with considerable accuracy, the best modern determination of the velocity of light being 186,270 miles per second. Now, the Earth is travelling around its orbit with a velocity of about 18½ miles per second in a direction which is constantly changing from day to day. Pondering over his observations to which we allude later, Bradley saw that to receive the light of a star at the centre of the field of his telescope, which of course is being carried around with the Earth, he must point his telescope in a slightly different direction from that in which it would be pointed if the Earth were stationary.

A simple and familiar analogy will serve as an illustration; if the rain is falling vertically and I am standing with an umbrella as protection, I naturally hold the umbrella vertically above me; if I am walking, I point it somewhat forward; if the rain is falling obliquely, I point it in a particular direction and at a particular angle (empirically determined as a result of long experience) depending on my rate of walking and the speed of the raindrops, and if I change direction I change the pointing of the umbrella. If we associate the streams of raindrops with rays of light and the umbrella with a telescope, we obtain the roughly equivalent astronomical parallel, so that to see a star in the centre of the field of the eye-piece we must point the telescope in a slightly different direction from the direction which would be set if the Earth were actually motionless.

In Fig. 10 we indicate the centre of the field of the telescope by the intersection, O, of two perpendicular "wires" in the focal plane of the eye-piece. Bradley's observations were, as stated, made with a stationary telescope and so the effect of aberration was thrown into the positions of the star relative to O in Fig. 10. If we suppose that the observations were made at intervals throughout a year, then the star's observed positions would lie on the curve shown in the figure, this curve being different, in certain important essentials, from that anticipated if the changes in the star's position were due entirely to distance-effects. The curve, actually observed, furnished the clue to the new phenomenon. Bradley failed in his original purpose of measuring the distance of Gamma Draconis but nevertheless he was rewarded with a success as remarkable as it was unexpected.

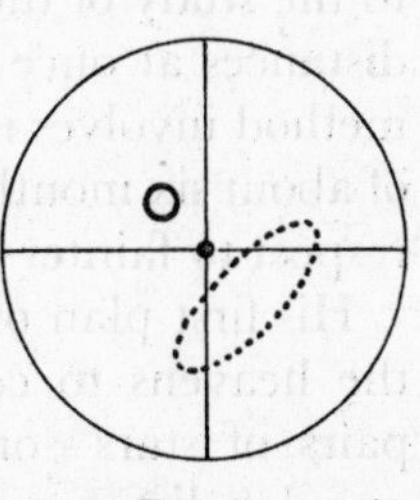

FIG. 10

The next important attempt at measuring a star's distance was undertaken by Sir William Herschel, one of the most distinguished astronomers of all time. Herschel, born in 1738, had started his active life at the age of 15 as a musician in the band of the Hanoverian Guards but after four years of military life he came to England, earning at first a precarious livelihood as a teacher of music. On being appointed organist at the famous Octagon Chapel at Bath, his fortunes rapidly improved. But his musical successes did not interfere with his thirst for knowledge in other fields ; the study of mathematics led him to astronomy and to astronomical observation, and later still to the manufacture of his own telescopes.

The long history of astronomy has nothing to show equal to, or even distantly approaching, the indefatigable zeal and enthusiastic application displayed by Herschel. On March 13, 1781, he discovered the planet Uranus—all the other planets then known had been familiar to the watchers of the heavens from remote ages—and the addition of a new member of the solar family was in itself an event of the greatest importance. A year later Herschel abandoned music for the stars and thereafter, as Royal Astronomer, he devoted all his time and energy to the study of the heavens. The problem of measuring stellar distances at once engaged his attention. As we have seen the method involves measuring the change of direction, at intervals of about six months, shown by the star under consideration with respect to fainter—and presumably more distant—stars.

His first plan of campaign was to make a careful scrutiny of the heavens to collect the requisite information about likely pairs of stars—or double stars, as we may call them ; the angular distance apart of the members (or *components*) of a pair and the direction in which the fainter component lay with respect to the brighter were measured with the skill and accuracy of which long practice had made him a master. By 1785 he had published two catalogues of over seven hundred double stars some of which had been recognised as such by earlier observers.

Having laid the groundwork for a systematic attempt to measure stellar distances, Herschel failed to achieve success, but, like Bradley, he made an unexpected discovery of the utmost moment to astronomy. Re-observing many of the double stars in his catalogues, Herschel obtained unmistakable evidence that several of his pairs were physically connected in the sense that the fainter component of such a double star appeared to be revolving around the brighter component in precisely the same way as that in which the Moon revolves around the Earth or a planet around the Sun. He even succeeded in deducing the periods of revolution in certain cases ; for example, the period for the double star Castor was estimated to be about 340 years.

Plate I (c), facing page 32, shows three photographs of a well-known double star, Krüger 60 ; it is easily seen that the star of the pair with the smaller image appears to be circling round its immediate neighbour ; between 1908 and 1920 it has completed about a quarter of its revolution, from which it may be estimated roughly that the period of revolution is about 48 years (the accurate value is 50 years). From the existence of such double stars—*binary* stars, as they are called, to distinguish them from an optical double, that is, a pair of stars that *appear* close together in the sky although one member of the pair may be 100 times farther off in space than the other—the inference followed that in the depths of space the law of gravitation operates just as it operates in the solar system to bind the planets in their orbits around the Sun.

And so a great new department of observational astronomy —the study of binary stars—was inaugurated, the results of which have had significant repercussions in the whole field of astronomy. We mention here the most important piece of information accruing from the study of a binary star namely, the measurement of the mass of the binary system and in many cases, as a result of other considerations, the mass of each component of the binary star. We thus can weigh the stars in a celestial balance, as it were, and perhaps surprisingly, they prove to be little different from the Sun as regards mass. The masses of the great majority of the stars are between one-half and five times the mass of the Sun ; the least massive star known from measurement of the kind indicated is about one-seventh of the mass of the Sun—this is the fainter component of Krüger 60—while a few exceptional stars have masses not far short of a hundred times the mass of the Sun.

Herschel's discovery of gravitational stellar systems was perhaps not altogether unexpected. Some years earlier the Rev. John Mitchell had made the suggestion roughly to this effect that if 10,000 of the brightest stars were scattered indiscriminately over the sky the chance of any two being found as close together as the components of an average binary would be extremely small and the probability against this occurring as regards even the relatively small number of double stars known at the time was so overwhelming that he felt certain that many of these pairs would prove to be " systems of bodies revolving about each other ".

This application of the doctrine of probability may be illustrated in a simple way. Suppose that aeroplanes are flying in all directions in the dark over Lincolnshire, say, and that from each aeroplane a single dummy bomb is dropped at any arbitrary moment according to the whim of the pilot. If two thousand bombs are dropped quite indiscriminately the chances are that we should find one in roughly each square mile of the county on the average and if we found two bombs within a few inches of one another we should regard this as a rather remarkable coincidence ; but if we found a hundred of such pairs the idea of coincidence would be out of the question and no doubt we should infer that a hundred aircraft had each dropped two bombs simultaneously.

Since Herschel's times thousands of binary stars—triple stars, quadruple stars and even sextuple stars are not uncommon—have been discovered and although estimates vary it seems certain that on a very conservative reckoning at least one star out of ten is really a binary or a multiple star.

Before passing to the first genuine measurement of a stellar distance, we may pause for a moment to consider one or two estimates that in some ways were informative. From the observations of the new star which appeared in 1572 the famous Danish astronomer Tycho Brahe inferred that the star must be more distant than the Moon—a result apparently of little consequence but yet of considerable importance in mediaeval astronomy, for it disposed of the Aristotelian idea of the unchangeability of the heavens.

Another attempt at estimating the distance of a star—in this case Arcturus—was based on the principle that if the Sun and the star were physically identical in every way except in the matter of distance, then the ratio of the brightness of the Sun to the brightness of Arcturus would provide the means of calculating the star's distance. The principal difficulty arises, of course, in comparing the almost incomparably greater brightness of the Sun with the brightness of Acturus under circumstances which preclude direct comparison. However, the conclusion was reached that Arcturus must be about 3¼ million times farther off than the Sun, a surprisingly accurate estimate when we state that the modern result derived from direct measurements is about 2½ million times the Sun's distance—that is to say, 2½ million astronomical units or about 230 million million miles.

Let us consider now how an astronomer, setting out for the first time on this evidently difficult operation of measuring a star's distance, selects the object on which he is going to lavish so much of his observational skill. Naturally, he wishes to have some assurance beforehand that if the operation is practicable for the nearest stars then the selected star should be of this category. One criterion is apparent brightness ; if all the stars are built on exactly the same model, like motor-cars issuing from a mass-production factory, then the brightest stars are likely also to be the nearest. We now know that this assumption is very far from the truth and that, in fact, the stars vary enormously in candle-power ; accordingly, this criterion is not a safe guide although, a century or more ago, its reasonableness was almost a matter of faith.

A second criterion is based on proper-motion, the rate at which a star changes its position in the sky relative to the background of the very faint and presumably distant stars. Suppose from an eminence we can see two parallel straight and level roads one, say, half a mile away and the other two miles away ; if we watch the traffic proceeding along each road, we shall notice that a motor-car travelling along the nearer road changes its direction with respect to the fixed objects of the landscape—telephone poles, trees, etc.—much more rapidly than a car travelling along the more distant road ; further, if we take the averages of all such observational results for a large number of cars of all types on the nearer road and also a similar average for the more distant road we shall find that, on the whole, the average rate of change of direction on the nearer road is about four times that on the other road. Now the astronomer is in the position of being able to measure proper motion—as we have seen on page 22—that is, the rate at which a star changes its direction in the sky with respect to the very distant faint stars ; and considering two stars that have very widely different values of proper motion he concludes that the star with the larger proper motion is very probably nearer than the other, an implicit assumption being that the speeds of the stars (expressed in miles per second) at right angles to the line of sight are not greatly different just as, in our example, we might suppose the speeds of the motor-cars on both roads to be within the range of twenty to fifty miles per hour.

This assumption about the transverse speeds of the stars was a reasonable working hypothesis which, of course, could only be verified in this form—as it was in essentials—when a considerable amount of accurate information relating to stellar distances had been collected.

A third criterion relates to the details associated with binary stars. Suppose we have two such systems for which the planes of revolution of the components are, to take the simplest case, at right angles to the line of sight ; suppose further that the periods of revolution are the same, say a hundred years, and that the masses of the two systems are the same, from which we can conclude from the laws of dynamics—we omit the arguments—that the average distances (in miles) between the pairs of components are identical. If one of these systems is much nearer to us than the other, the two components in the former will appear farther apart in the sky than the two components of the latter, just as two neighbouring telephone poles on the nearer of our two roads subtend at the observer a larger angle than a pair of neighbouring poles on the farther road and in the same direction. Again, of two systems of the same mass but with different periods of revolution, the components of the system with the shorter period will be closer together in space than the components of the system with the longer period, just as the Earth with its period of revolution of one year is nearer the Sun than Jupiter with its period of revolution of twelve years ; if the two systems are equally " open ", the first must be nearer to us than the second. Considerations such as these enable us to arrive at the general principle that an " open " binary with a comparatively short period—as the periods of binaries go—is, almost certainly, very much nearer than a "close" binary with an equal or longer period of revolution.

These three criteria—or the first two, if the star is single—enable us to make a fairly good guess as to whether the observation of a star is likely to be productive of a satisfactory result, having due regard to the capabilities of the instrumental means at our disposal. It is fortunate for the progress of astronomical science that the distances of the stars are no greater than they are; if they had all been a hundred times farther off it is certain that even at the present time we should have had in our possession comparatively little acurate information about their distances, for even the nearest star on this hypothesis would barely yield a reliable measurement of its distance with the telescopic power of the present day. A century ago it was only a few of the nearest stars that came within reach, so to speak, of the instruments and methods of the time, and even now the fundamental principles of measuring a star's distance can be successfully applied only to a few thousand of our nearest stellar neighbours. To explore the greater depths of space other methods must be developed but these rest intrinsically on the results of the fundamental method with which we are now about to deal as regards its earliest successes.

The star about which the main theme of the present chapter revolves is 61 Cygni—No. 61 in Flamsteed's numerical assignment of the stars in the constellation of the Swan. It is, first of all, a very open binary star, each component being of the fifth magnitude and therefore not notably bright in the sense of the first criterion; however, a century ago it was impossible to derive an accurate estimate of the period of revolution—now known to be about 700 years—and so the third criterion played little part in its selection.

Fig. 11 shows the position of 61 Cygni in the constellation of Cygnus.

At this point we introduce the name of Bessel who by his successful observations of 61 Cygni gave astronomers the first reliable information concerning the vast distances of even the nearest objects in the stellar universe. It was mainly the second criterion that induced Bessel to engage on the long series of observations that were crowned with success in 1838. Because of its very large proper motion—the largest known at the time and amounting to five seconds of arc per annum *—61 Cygni was familiarly known in the astronomical world as the " flying star ". It therefore seemed to Bessel to give every promise of being one of the nearest stars in the sky, and so it proved.

Bessel, born in 1784 at Minden in Germany, was early apprenticed to a mercantile firm in Bremen and, fired with the laudable ambition of rising in his profession, he studied in his spare time such languages as would be useful in the East Indian

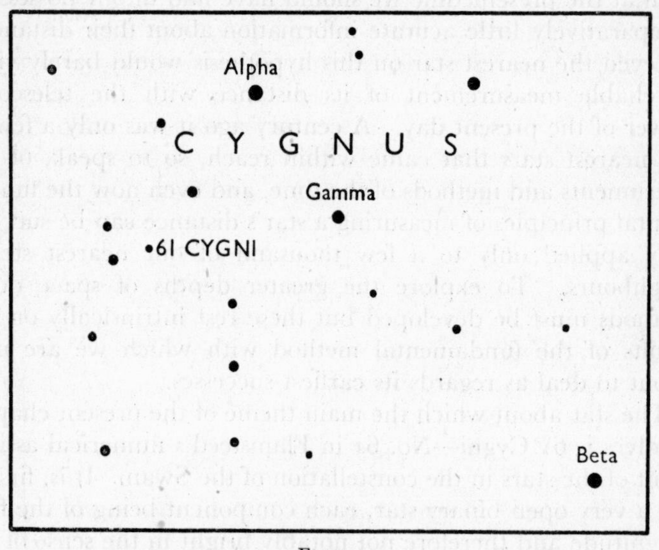

FIG. 11

trade in which his firm was engaged. He also perfected himself in the art of navigation ; navigation led naturally to an interest in astronomy and thereafter to mathematics. At the age of twenty Bessel had succeeded in deriving the orbit of Halley's comet from the observations made at its appearance in 1607 and he at once became a person of European reputation. Two years later he abandoned a commercial career, with glittering prizes not far distant, for a humble post as assistant

* This proper motion is such that the star would move over the background of the faint stars by an amount equal to the angular diameter of the Moon in about 380 years.

in an observatory. Within a few years he was director of the new observatory at Königsberg where many of his important discoveries were made.

In 1837 Bessel began his observations of 61 Cygni according to the method already described—the method of measuring with reference to one or more faint stars the change of direction of a nearby star against the background of the faint stars as the Earth moved round in its orbit. His telescope was of unique character, known as a heliometer, and capable of the highest precision attainable at the time. In December 1838, Bessel published the result of his observations ; 61 Cygni was at a distance of about 600,000 astronomical units or close to sixty million million miles. At last astronomers had authentic information about the vast distances of even our nearest stellar neighbours.

It frequently happens in science that when, after a long period of apparent stagnation and even frustration, the moment comes for some spectacular advance to be made, success comes almost simultaneously to more than one pioneer ; and so it proved in the present instance. Within two months of Bessel's publication of the distance of 61 Cygni came the announcement of Henderson's success in measuring the distance of Alpha Centauri, one of the brightest stars in the southern sky.

Henderson's career bore several marks of resemblance to Bessel's. Born in Dundee and in early life a solicitor's clerk, he rapidly obtained a reputation in astronomical circles for his scientific attainments to such purpose that he was appointed in 1831 to the directorship of the Observatory at the Cape of Good Hope ; however, he remained there only a short time, returning to his native country as Astronomer Royal for Scotland. At the Cape he had made a series of observations of Alpha Centauri—not however for the specific purpose of measuring its distance—but from these observations he was enabled after his return to Scotland to deduce the distance of the star. There is no doubt that if he had discussed the Cape observations without unreasonable delay he would have had the distinction, so rightly adjudged to Bessel, of being the first to bridge successfully the vast gap between us and the stars.

If Henderson, when at the Cape, had set out deliberately to

measure the distance of a star it is certain that he could not have chosen one more suitable than Alpha Centauri according to the criteria mentioned. In the first place it is, to the naked eye, the third brightest star in the southern sky ; second, its proper motion is very large, although not quite so large as that of 61 Cygni, being about $\frac{3}{4}$ that of the latter ; third, it is a very " open " binary with the short period of 79 years. In all three criteria it encourages the most sanguine expectations that it is one of the nearest stars. Henderson's observations showed that the distance of Alpha Centauri is about 200,000 astronomical units or nearly 20 million million miles ; modern measurements have increased the distance by about 30 per cent. but even so Alpha Centauri is our nearest stellar neighbour. It may be added that Alpha Centauri is now known to be a triple system, consisting of the bright components forming the binary referred to, and a faint star of the eleventh magnitude about two degrees from the close pair.

In 1840 a third success in measuring the distance of a star followed the achievements of Bessel and Henderson. At Pulkowa Observatory, destroyed during the seige of Leningrad in the second world war, Struve succeeded in measuring with fair accuracy the distance of the bright star Vega, his result being about one-half that derived from the best modern observations.

The congratulations of the whole astronomical world to Bessel on his memorable achievement—and the liveliest optimism for the speedy extension of knowledge of stellar distances—are fitly summarised in the following piece of sonorous Victorian prose taken from the address of Sir John Herschel—son of the discoverer of Uranus, and President of the Royal Astronomical Society—on the occasion of the award of the Society's Gold Medal to Bessel in 1841. " I congratulate you and myself that we have lived to see the great and hitherto impossible barrier to our excursions into the sidereal universe—that barrier against which we have chafed so long and so vainly—almost simultaneously overleaped at three different points. It is the greatest and most glorious triumph which practical astronomy has ever witnessed. Perhaps I ought not to speak so strongly—perhaps I should hold some reserve in favour of the bare possibility that it may all be an illusion and that further researches, as they have repeatedly before, so may now fail to substantiate this noble result. But I confess myself unequal to such prudence under such excitement. Let us rather accept the joyful omens of the time and trust that, as the barrier has begun to yield, it will speedily be prostrated. Such results are among the fairest flowers of civilisation."

Although by the end of the nineteenth century a few additional stars yielded up the secrets of their distances, the contemporary observational technique proved inadequate for a really deep penetration into space ; the optimism of 1841 was sadly disappointed and it was only when the much more accurate photographic methods came into use at the beginning of the present century that rapid progress in this fundamental problem of astronomy could be achieved.

To the reader Struve's result may not seem very significant owing to the apparent lack of accuracy ; to this it may be justly replied that when the immense difficulty of the operation is realised—for Vega is nearly three times farther away than 61 Cygni and about six times farther away than Alpha Centauri—Struve's achievement can then be seen in its true proportions. A simple illustration adapted from one of Sir David Gill's lectures may make the matter clearer ; Struve's task was roughly equivalent to measuring the angle subtended by the diameter of a threepenny piece situated at a distance of about a dozen miles. Gill himself continued with fair success the work of ascertaining the distances of a few stars visible from the Observatory at the Cape of Good Hope. In the lecture alluded to, Gill made use of the analogy of the threepenny piece just mentioned. At the conclusion of the lecture the chairman, referring to the astronomical achievements that had just been described, added the remark that perhaps the item that had impressed him most was the anxiety of his Scottish friend, Gill, about a threepenny piece a dozen miles away!

The earliest pioneer in the photographic method of observations was Pritchard, the Savilian Professor of Astronomy at Oxford, whose main claim to fame in this connection was his demonstration of the advantages of photography over the visual observations still practised by astronomers in many parts of the globe. The need for more powerful photographic telescopes was of course realised and the first ambitious programme of measuring stellar distances was undertaken in 1900 by A. R. Hinks and H. N. Russell at Cambridge with the Sheepshanks telescope which was specially designed for the purpose. A similar programme was inaugurated a little later by Schlesinger in America and since then about a dozen observatories all over the globe have been engaged—not all continuously—in this important work. Today we know with fair accuracy the distances of perhaps 5000 stars, photographically observed according to the fundamental principles described earlier. Even so, this basic method allows us to explore the stellar system only to a comparatively small distance from the Sun ; to cast the fathom-line farther into space we require to find new methods ; these, it must be said at once, are built up on the knowledge of stellar distances so painstakingly garnered by the three or four generations of astronomers since Bessel's time, using the same geometrical principles—although not the same instrumental techniques—as that master of nineteenth century astronomy.

Earlier in this chapter we have expressed the distance of 61 Cygni as so many astronomical units or so many million million miles. It is clearly desirable in dealing with these immense distances to introduce a new unit and for our purpose the most suitable is the *light-year.** As we have seen (page 36) light travels through space with a speed of 186,270 miles *per second* ; as there are 31½ million seconds in a year, the distance travelled by light *in a year* is easily found to be about 5·9 million million miles ; this distance is called a *light-year*, which is comparable with the distance of the nearest star ; the distance of Alpha Centauri is, in fact, 4⅓ light-years, and the distance of 61 Cygni is nearly 11 light-years. As we have stated previously, the direct method of measuring stellar distances does not take us very far into the depths of space, perhaps as far as 500 light-years ; this is a mere step compared with the distance of 500 million light-years explored by the 100-inch telescope of Mt. Wilson Observatory and with double that distance explored by the new 200-inch telescope on Mount Palomar in California. We shall later discuss how this farther penetration into the

* The astronomer's unit is called *the parsec*, equivalent to 3¼ light-years.

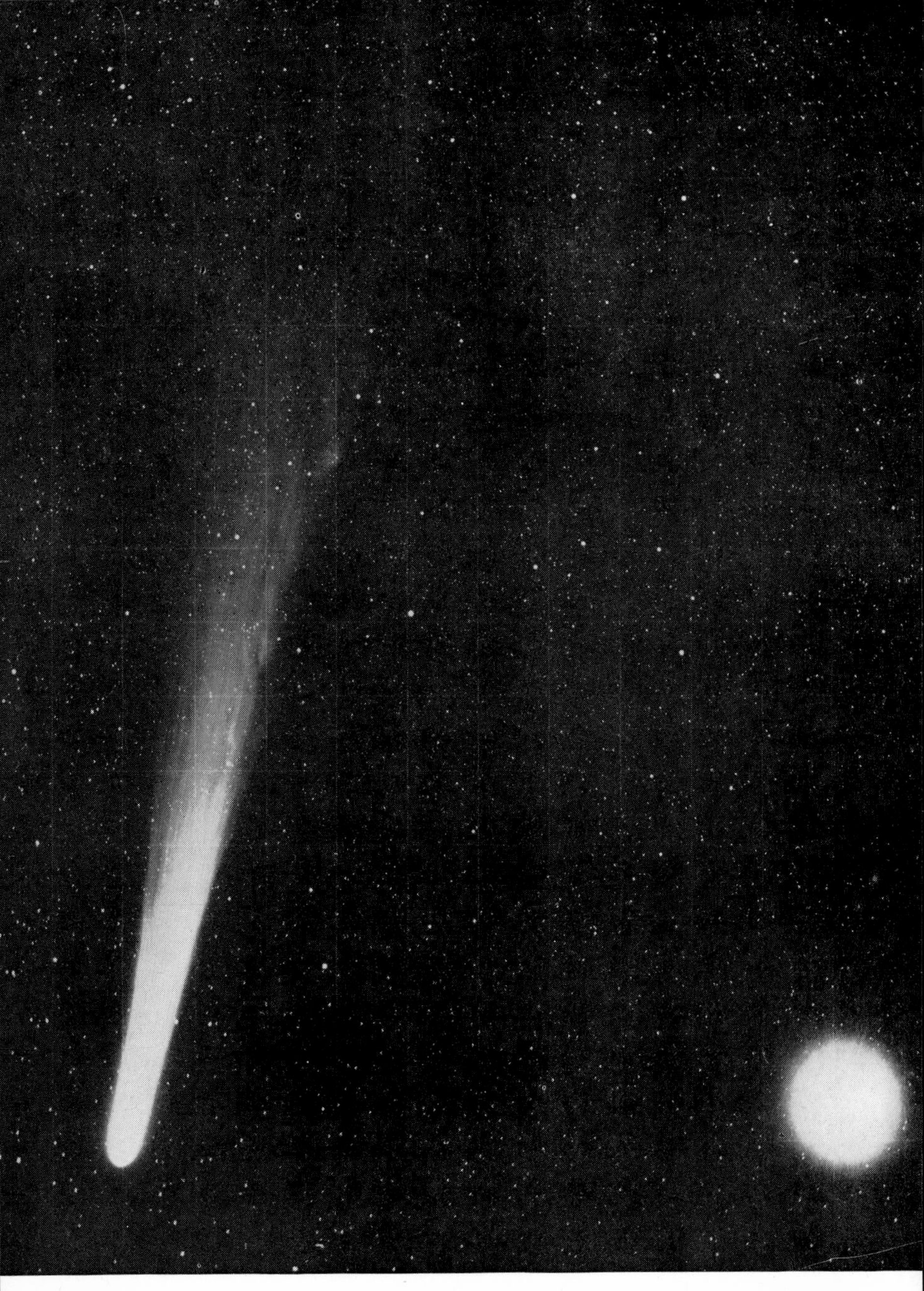

III. Halley's Comet in 1910. The large image in the bottom right-hand corner is that of the planet Venus

(*Union Observatory, Johannesburg*)

D

IV(a). Sky spectrum showing D lines of Sodium
(*Cambridge Observatory*)

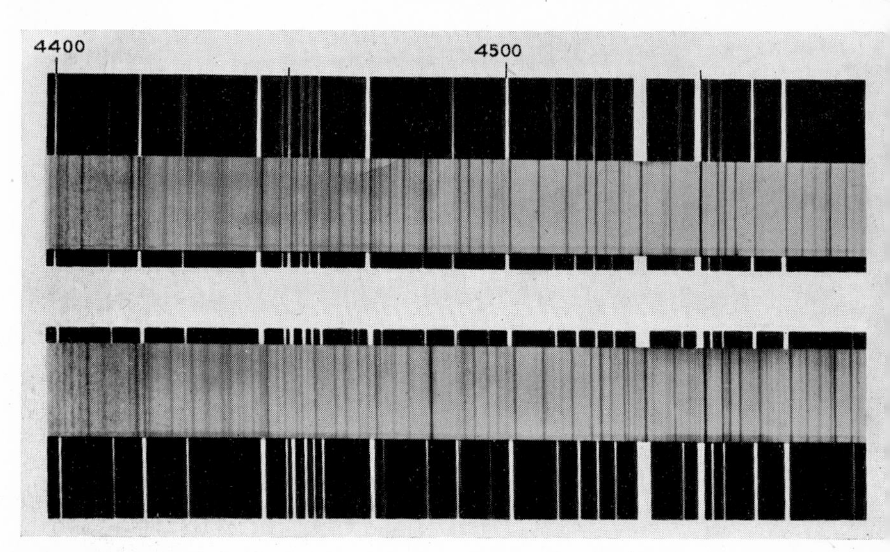

IV(b). Spectra of the bright component of μ Orionis showing variable displacements of absorption lines (dark) with respect to the lines (white) of the comparison spectrum

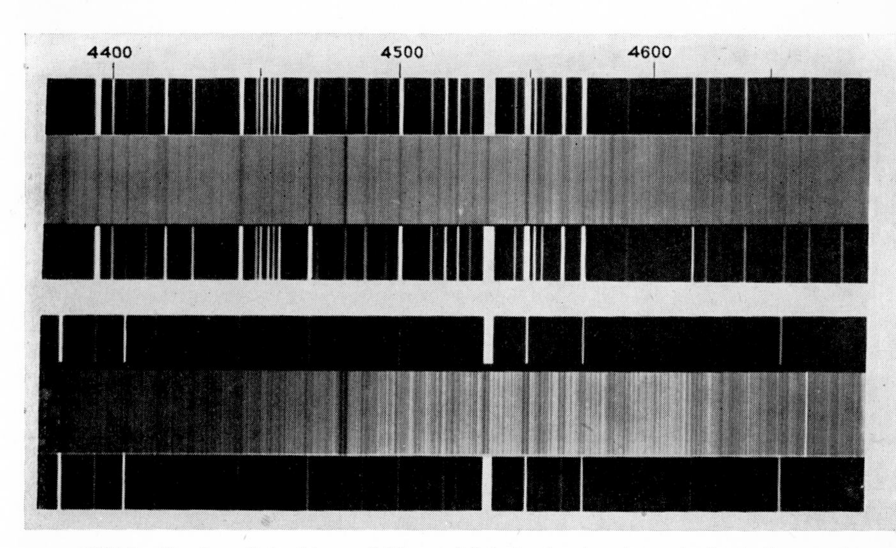

IV(c). Spectra of the binary ζ Ursae Majoris showing (upper) single lines and (lower) the lines doubled
(*Yerkes Observatory*)

depth of space has been effected but it is well to emphasise again that these almost incredible achievements depend basically on the apparently more modest successes nearer home, of which 61 Cygni provided the first example.

The use of the term light-year has one advantage, for it enables us to think of the vast stellar distances in terms of a kind of historical setting. When we look at 61 Cygni, the light which enters our eye, say in 1950, has been travelling through space since those eventful days when Hitler unleashed the dogs of war. A modest star in the firmament may suggest to a patriotic Scotsman that the light which now enters his eye has been traversing space since the date of the Battle of Bannockburn. Another star may be so far away that its light, now enabling us to observe it, must have been emitted about the time that Julius Caesar was crossing the narrow straits in his first invasion of Britain. And what of the far more distant objects, the great star clusters and the nebulae from ten thousand to five hundred million light-years away? Here we reach into prehistoric times and into the remotest past, from which we perhaps attain some modicum of understanding of the immense scale of the Universe.

We further reflect that when we speak of observing 61 Cygni in 1950 we appear to suggest that this famous binary system is actually in existence in 1950 as we describe it then; for all we know, a celestial catastrophe at the present moment may have overtaken it, and the news—borne on the wings of light—will not reach us for eleven more years. It is thus evident that we cannot obtain a picture of the Universe as it is at a particular instant; we are in much the same position as the hypothetical historian who is trying to describe the state of Europe in 1950 when all his available information is restricted to events occurring between the Stone Age and the Norman Conquest.

We now go on to describe part of the rich harvest reaped as a result of our knowledge of stellar distances. In the first chapter we discussed the relative brightnesses of the stars as we observe them in the sky and we introduced the term *apparent magnitude* as a convenient means whereby we can arrange the stars in order of brightness as they are seen in the sky. But when we reflect that the stars are at all sorts of distances from us the apparent magnitude of a star tells us nothing about its candle-power; for all we know a first-magnitude such star as Vega may be of less candle-power than a sixth-magnitude star barely visible to the naked eye, just as the light of a motor head-lamp a few feet away appears brighter than a powerful lighthouse lantern ten miles away, an illusion that is quickly dissipated if we observe the head-lamp and lantern when both are at the same distance from us. We can of course arrange for the head-lamp to be placed in close proximity to the lighthouse and if we make our observations say at a distance of a mile we can, with suitable optical equipment, deduce that the candle-power of the lantern is, say, a thousand times greater than that of the head-lamp—the former will, in fact, now appear to be a thousand times brighter than the latter.

When we come to try to compare the candle-power of two stars, we cannot of course move one star about in space—as it was possible to move the head-lamp—until it is at the same distance from us as the other; but we can easily calculate, when the distances of the two stars are known, how much one star would be brighter than the other if they were equidistant from us. To compare the candle-power of any number of stars it is evidently desirable to make our calculations with reference to a standard distance which is arbitrarily taken to be $32\frac{1}{2}$ light-years.*

Consider as an example the brighter component of 61 Cygni; in the telescope it is seen as a star of apparent magnitude 5·6. We have then to find out how bright the star would be if it were removed from its present distance of 11 light-years to the standard distance which is nearly three times farther away; evidently, the star would appear fainter and its new magnitude would be numerically larger than its present magnitude of 5·6, and this increase is found by calculation to be 2·4. Accordingly, the star's magnitude at the standard distance would be $5{\cdot}6 + 2{\cdot}4$, that is 8·0. The magnitude of a star calculated for the standard distance is called the *absolute magnitude* † of the

* Or 10 parsecs.

† The choice of the adjective "absolute" is perhaps unfortunate, since the selection of the standard distance involved is arbitrary; although "standard magnitude" would be a much more suitable expression, the use of "absolute magnitude" has been so firmly established that a revision of nomenclature is hardly likely to be countenanced.

star ; we say then that the absolute magnitude of the brighter component of 61 Cygni is 8·0.

We are now in a position to compare the intrinsic brightness of stars when we know their apparent magnitudes and distances ; for example, if the absolute magnitudes of two stars A and B are 3·0 and 8·0 respectively—these, it is well to recall would be the magnitudes if the stars were both at the standard distance from us—then, since a difference of 5 magnitudes corresponds to a brightness-ratio of 100 to 1, we conclude that star A is 100 times more luminous than star B : we can express this differently by saying that the candle-power of A is 100 times the candle-power of B.

As a result of rather intricate observations the absolute magnitude of the Sun has been found ; if our luminary were removed to a distance of 32½ light-years from the Earth—that is about two million times its present distance from the Earth—it would be seen as a star of magnitude 4·8 which, by definition, is the Sun's absolute magnitude. We can now compare the intrinsic brightness of the Sun and the brighter component of 61 Cygni ; the absolute magnitudes are 4·8 and 8·0 respectively, with a difference of magnitude of 3·2. The formula for converting difference of magnitude into ratio of brightness gives the result that the Sun is about 19 times more luminous than the brighter component of 61 Cygni. It is convenient to have a single word to convey the meaning of the rather cumbrous expression " intrinsic brightness " ; accordingly, we shall adopt the term *luminosity*.

It is found that the absolute magnitudes of the great majority of the stars are included within the range -5 to $+15$, with the Sun's absolute magnitude of 4·8 occupying a nearly central position. Consider a star A, of absolute magnitude $-5·0$, and the Sun ; the difference of absolute magnitude is 9·8 which shows that A is nearly 10,000 times more luminous than the Sun. Consider a star B, of absolute magnitude $+15·0$, and the Sun ; the difference of absolute magnitudes is 10·2 which shows that the Sun is more than 10,000 times more luminous than B. The stars thus vary enormously in luminosity, the star A being 100 million times more luminous than the star B ; the Sun is, evidently, a very ordinary star. The range of stellar luminosity is very much like the range of candle-power of a searchlight at one end of the range and a glow-worm at the other end, the Sun being represented in an intermediate position by an electric torch.

The stars of high luminosity are called *giants* and those of low candle-power are called *dwarfs* ; although there is no precise dividing line between the two classes it may assist the reader to regard stars within the range -5 to $+2$ as giants, and stars within the range $+2$ to $+15$ as dwarfs ; the Sun is definitely reckoned as a dwarf star.

The terms " giants " and " dwarfs " suggest great variations in the *sizes* of the stars, and this is found to be the case. Red stars, for example, are sharply divided into two categories, one of very great luminosity, the other of feeble luminosity ; a red giant is perhaps one million times more luminous than a particular red dwarf. If we assume that the surface-temperatures of the two stars are the same, so that the rate of emission of light from a square yard of surface is the same for both stars, then it is clear that the immense diversity of luminosity depends on the relative surface-areas of the two stars ; the surface-area of the giant must be, in fact, one million times that of the dwarf, from which it follows that the diameter of the giant is a thousand times that of the dwarf. So far as the red stars are concerned, the division into giants and dwarfs according to luminosity is also a division according to size.

We may mention here as a point of interest and without going into details—we discuss such matters in later chapters—that a knowledge of a star's distance, together with that of its proper motion, enables us to calculate the star's speed at right angles to the line of sight (the *transverse speed*, as it is called) in terms of familiar units. For example, if we take the proper motion of 61 Cygni to be 5 seconds of arc per annum its known distance enables us to calculate the transverse speed to be about 49 miles per second. As an individual result this may seem to be an item of, perhaps, passing interest but, later on, we shall see how a knowledge of stellar motions helps us in many diverse investigations.

As another example in which the knowledge of a star's distance can be of service in leading to more detailed information we mention that the study of elliptic orbits of binary stars enables us to derive the average separation (in miles or astronomical units) of the two components of a binary system. The careful investigation of 61 Cygni by Dr. Alan Fletcher shows that the two stars are separated on the average by a distance of about 80 astronomical units—that is, by a distance of 80 times the distance of the Earth from the Sun—or nearly 7500 million miles. The average separation of the two bright components of Alpha Centauri is about 23 astronomical units—about 40 per cent. greater than the distance of the planet Uranus from the Sun ; the faint component, alluded to previously, is at the vast distance of something like 10,000 astronomical units from the two bright stars of the system.

Before leaving 61 Cygni we take this opportunity of referring to a recent discovery associated with this star. Astronomers are frequently asked if there are any other systems of planets in the Universe resembling the solar family and the answer can be given that even with the biggest telescope in the world it would be impossible to see a system such as our own even if it were no farther off than the nearest star ; for example, a hypothetical observer as far away as Alpha Centauri would see the Sun as a star—of roughly the brightness of Capella as seen from the Earth—but Jupiter and the other great planets would be completely invisible.

But a heavenly body can, on occasion, make its presence known in ways other than through the medium of its light, for example, through its gravitational attraction on another body. Perhaps the most famous instance relates to the discovery, in 1846, of an unknown planet—Neptune—because it was sufficiently massive to alter, by its gravitational attraction, the positions of Uranus by unmistakable amounts. The next chapter will deal in detail with a similar instance, farther afield in space, which has some points of resemblance with the discovery of a body of planetary or sub-stellar mass in the binary system of 61 Cygni.

Systematic observations of the relations between the two components of the binary began in 1830. From the averages of all available observations over periods of two years, roughly, it was seen that the fainter component B appeared to describe

(Fig. 12) a comparatively smooth part XY of an elliptic orbit with respect to the brighter component A (it will be recollected that the period of a complete revolution of B around A is deduced to be 700 years); the dots between X and Y then refer to the two-yearly averages. Recently, the extensive series of observations of Dr. Strand, plotted at intervals of a month or two, show that the path of B around A is represented by a wavy curve of the kind shown between Y and Z in the figure. It is then inferred that either A or B is itself a double system (for simplicity we suppose it is B), the other member C being invisible, although exercising its gravitational attraction on B with the observational effects shown.

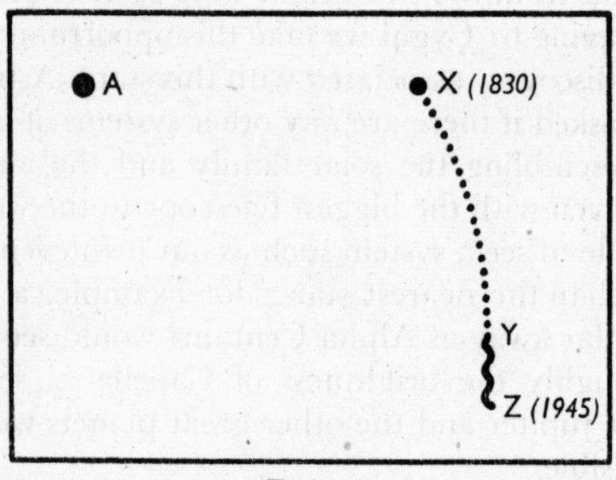

Fig. 12

From the characteristics of the wavy line it is deduced that the dark body C revolves around B in a period of about two years—in much the same way as the Moon revolves around the Earth—and that the mass of C is about one-seventieth of the mass of the Sun or about fifteen times the mass of Jupiter, the most massive planet in the Solar System. We have already mentioned in connection with Krüger 60 that the mass of the fainter component is about one-seventh that of the Sun and this is a feebly luminous star; it is certain, too, that bodies of still smaller mass must be barely self-luminous. It would then seem that the unseen body in the system of 61 Cygni is nearer to the physical state of a planet—a cold non-luminous body—than to the state of a body enjoying the status of a star capable of radiating heat and light. Although the existence of bodies of similar mass has been inferred in the case of two or three other stars it may seem advisable to suspend judgment until a longer series of observations on 61 Cygni and these stars is available.

The question as to the existence or non-existence of other planetary systems can be approached from another angle. We know of the existence of one planetary system—our own—but despite the ingenuity of different astronomers in seeking an explanation of its origin we are still far from being able to assert that the Solar System came into being as the consequence of such and such circumstances. If the set of circumstances is purely accidental in character and not likely to apply to any other star we must conclude that the Solar System is unique. If, on the other hand, observational astronomy can assert beyond dispute that there are planetary systems in stellar regions, perhaps valuable clues will be found to enable us, in due course, to obtain rather more than an inkling as to the way by which the Sun's family of planets came into existence ; in the present state of astronomy it would be merely uncritical optimism to go any further.

Chapter III

THE COMPANION OF SIRIUS

One of the differences inherent in the various kinds of terrestrial matter which we handle daily relates to density. A cubic foot of water, for example, weighs 62½ pounds and a cubic foot of iron weighs about 484 pounds—that is, about 7¾ times the weight of a cubic foot of water. Regarding water as a convenient standard substance with which we can compare the weights of other substances, volume for volume, we say that iron is 7¾ times *denser* than water ; and this property of iron in relation to the standard substance is called *density*. The densest terrestrial substance known is the comparatively rare element osmium which has a density of 22½ compared with water ; a cubic foot of osmium would accordingly weigh nearly 1500 pounds or about five-eighths of a ton. The density of gases is very much less than that of water and liquids in general ; for example a cubic foot of the air we breathe weighs rather less than a twelfth part of an ounce. Gases of course can be readily compressed—the pumping of air into the tyre of a motor car is a familiar instance—whereas, the application of pressure to liquids and solids can increase the density only in relatively insignificant proportions.

The relative degrees of compressibility of solids and liquids, on one hand, and of gases on the other are explained as follows. In a solid such as iron the atoms * are already jammed tightly together, like the grains of sand in a block of sandstone, and it is impossible by the application of pressure to force them closer together except to an almost insignificant degree. On the

* The structure of an *atom* will be described later ; meanwhile we may regard an atom of iron, for example, as the smallest entity with which are associated the characteristic physical and chemical properties of that element. A *molecule* is a closely-bound association of two or more atoms ; for example, the molecule of water consists of two atoms of hydrogen and one of oxygen forming a stable unit under ordinary terrestrial conditions ; many gaseous elements exist under ordinary conditions in the molecular state—for example, the smallest discrete " particle " of oxygen in the air is a closely-knit combination of two atoms of oxygen forming a molecule.

other hand the atoms of a gas or the molecules of atmospheric air, for example, are very far from being in contact and when pressure is applied the atoms or molecules can be compressed more tightly ; the density of the gas is consequently increased but never to a degree under normal conditions exceeding the density of the familiar liquids or solids.

At first sight we might imagine that the various kinds of stuff of which the Universe is composed are likely to have densities similar to those of the familiar terrestrial substances. The stars, as stated earlier, are gaseous and if we consider the enormous pressure to which the central core of the star is exposed—for the core has to sustain the weight of the stellar gas above it—we might expect the compression of the central gas to be such that its density would be increased very considerably indeed ; calculations, in fact, enable us to arrive at a reliable estimate of this central density. The mass and the dimensions of the Sun are known and the *average* density of the solar material is found to be just a little less than 1½ times that of water ; but, at the centre, the solar gas is compressed to a density of about 75 times that of water—more than three times the density of the densest element with which we are familiar in our laboratories. Such is indeed something far outside our normal experience. [illegible] another example the average density of the brighter component of the binary star Capella is just about twice the density of the air we breathe, while the central density of this star is one-eighth that of water.

The high densities in the deep interiors of many of the stars such as the Sun seem to conflict with the gaseous state attributed to them, but later (page 82) we shall attempt to dispose of this apparent contradiction. Great as such densities are, they pale into insignificance with the density of the matter of which the Companion of Sirius is composed, for the average density of this star is about 65,000 times the density of water so that a cubic foot of the stellar material would weigh nearly 2000 tons ; or, putting it another way, the average density is such that a match-box could contain about a ton and a quarter of the stellar material. The central density must be much greater and, if we filled our match-box with a sample from the core of the star, it would weigh perhaps 50 tons.

It seems incredible that matter can exist of such fantastic density but the steps in the chain of reasoning have been subjected to such close and careful scrutiny that the conclusion cannot be challenged. The Companion of Sirius is indeed a remarkable star ; it is known as a *white dwarf*, a class of star known to number many members most of which have estimated densities greatly exceeding that of the Companion. Matter then can exist in the Universe in a state unfamiliar on the Earth and wholly unsuspected until the Companion of Sirius first laid bare the secret.

We have disclosed the end of the story the beginning of which goes back to the time of Hipparchus who, we recollect, compiled a catalogue of the positions of over a thousand stars so as to leave to posterity as accurate a record of the sky in his time as the crude observations of contemporary astronomy permitted, being impelled to do so by the appearance and subsequent disappearance of a " new " star. It is not known what expectations of possible change in the sky Hipparchus had in mind or vaguely suspected, but perhaps he would have been disappointed if he had been made aware that no fewer than nearly a score of centuries would have to roll away before his catalogue was able to furnish indisputable proof that the heavens were not immutable.

In 1718 a new era in astronomy began with Halley's discovery of proper motion. Hitherto practical astronomers were mainly concerned with improving instrumental technique so as to be able to increase the accuracy of star positions. Evidently it had not occurred to any one before Halley to compare the most recently observed positions of the principal stars with their positions measured one or more centuries before ; if this supposition is not exactly accurate, then it is certain that no changes in position had been detected. At the end of the sixteenth century, Giordano Bruno—who was later, in 1600, burnt at the stake in Rome for propagating heretical theological doctrines—had surmised that the stars were moving about in space and were not immobile like ships at anchor. This speculation, suggestive as it was, had not been followed up.

Then in 1718 came Halley's great discovery that the positions of three stars, Sirius, Aldebaran and Arcturus in their respective constellations were undoubtedly different from their positions in the time of Hipparchus. The face of the heavens was no longer unchangeable as asserted in Aristotelian doctrine, and what was true of Halley's three stars might be equally true, perhaps in less measure, of all the brighter stars, as Bruno surmised. Positional astronomy had now a major incentive other than the mere desire for increased accuracy, and soon the proper motions of many other bright stars were measured. The introduction of photographic methods has extended our knowledge of stellar motions to faint stars and now the earlier conception of a static universe has given way to one in which there is ceaseless movement ; the stars are no longer like ships anchored all over the wide ocean, they resemble ships going about their lawful occasions.

Halley's discovery may be illustrated in a simple way. Suppose Hipparchus had surveyed the principal mountain peaks with which he was acquainted ; and suppose that with the instruments available to him he was able to assign a latitude and longitude to each peak, collecting all the results of his survey in the form of a geographical catalogue. Many centuries later similar surveys were undertaken and Halley, we suppose, comparing the latest positions of several peaks with the positions assigned by his great predecessor, became convinced that three peaks had undoubtedly changed their positions ; just as if Ben Lomond had been proved to have been removed from a position near Stirling in the time of Hipparchus to its present position on the east shore of Loch Lomond, Ben Nevis had originally been at Inverness and Ben Ledi at Perth. The terrestrial surveyor in 1718 would have had a hard job to explain the apparently mysterious migration of the three mountains ; no doubt he would first attempt to put the blame on the ancient observations on the score of observational inaccuracy or of errors accidently introduced by the various scribes responsible for the transmission of the original manuscript ; if these suggestions proved to be unacceptable, he would perchance explain the three phenomena in terms of a convulsion of nature occurring no doubt in the dark ages.

In the case of the three stars Halley had only one explanation to offer ; each of the stars was moving in space and therefore this motion would be revealed as a progressive change of direction against the background of the fixed, or relatively immobile, stars in the immediate neighbourhood in the sky.

Fig. 13 illustrates diagrammatically the proper motion of Sirius (Alpha Canis Majoris) with reference to the fainter stars of the constellation ; A is the position of the star in the time of Hipparchus and B its position in the time of Halley. If Sirius is moving with a constant speed in space and in a constant direction—in the absence of information to the contrary this would be a reasonable hypothesis—then it would appear to change its position in the sky at substantially a uniform rate in its progress from A to B. The hypothesis could be tested by means of intermediate observations if such existed and, in due course, by means of later observations. For single stars the hypothesis is verified and we conclude that, even over the considerable periods of time during which accurate observations are available, there is no observational evidence of the kind with which we are dealing that single stars move in space other than in straight lines at constant speed. However, later on in the book (page 212) we shall see that this statement requires modification when intervals of time of the order of several millions of years are under consideration.

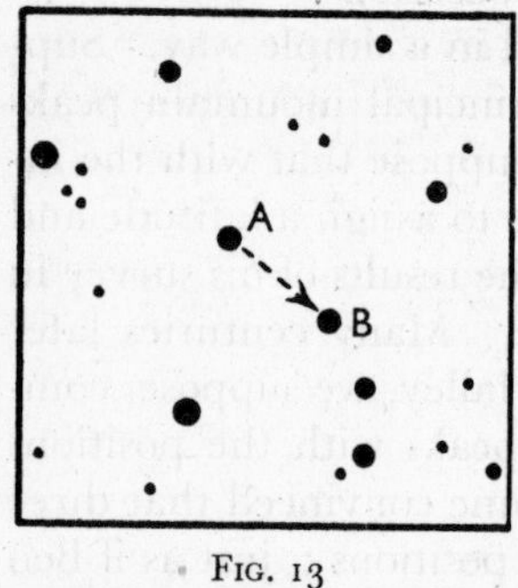

Fig. 13

We realise now that all the stars are moving in all sorts of directions with all sorts of speeds and as a consequence the configuration of any single constellation must be altering. It is not to be supposed that such changes in configuration are easily detectable in the course of a life-time or even longer. A Rip van Winkle who woke up from a sleep of a thousand years would not perceive any striking change in the configuration of the seven stars forming the well-known group of stars known as the " Plough " or " Charles's Wain " : but if his sleep had been a hundred times longer he could not fail to notice changes in the configuration of the seven stars. This is illustrated in the Fig. 14 (*a*) and (*b*), the first being the present appearance of the group and the second (derived from the present-day data) as it will be seen 100,000 years hence.

So far we have not given any indication as to the magnitude of the stellar speeds. If we know the distance of a star and also its proper motion we can easily calculate its *transverse* speed, that is, the speed perpendicular to the line of sight. This may

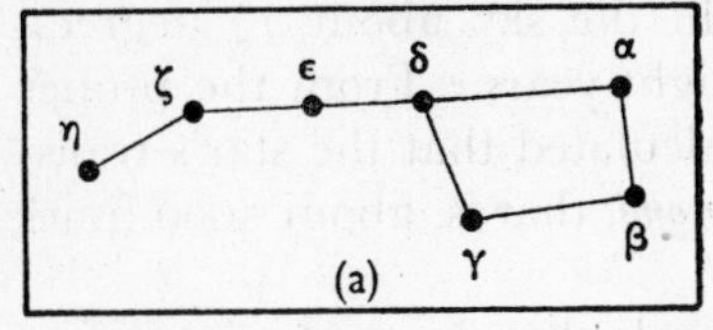

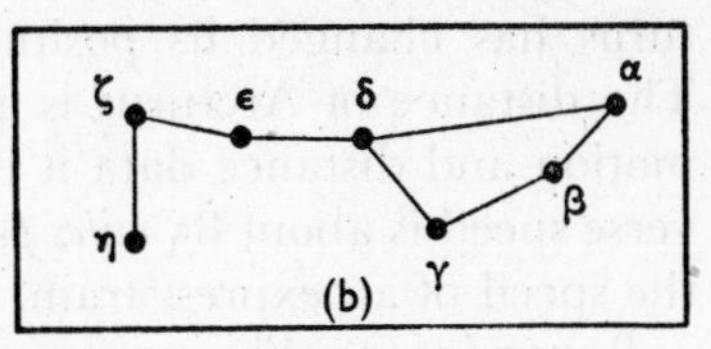

FIG. 14.—The "Plough": (*a*) at present, (*b*) 100,000 years hence

be illustrated by means of Fig. 15. Suppose from an eminence at O we can see a straight road AB and we observe the directions of a motor-car at the beginning and end of an interval of a minute; suppose these directions are OX and OY, and that the angle XOY is 1°. In the usual astronomical phraseology we should say that the proper motion is 1° per minute. In general the road will run obliquely to the direction OX and if we draw XZ perpendicular to OX the same proper motion will be deduced if the car had been travelling along a side road PQ at a speed which would take it from X to Z in one minute; this speed is evidently less than the speed which would be necessary to take the car along the road AB from X to Y in one minute. This latter speed corresponds to the star's speed in space relative to a stationary observer at O, and the speed represented by the passage over the distance XZ in one minute corresponds to the *transverse* speed of the star. If we know the distance between O and X we can easily calculate the car's transverse speed in miles per hour, but unless we know how the road AB is inclined to the direction of OX we cannot find out the

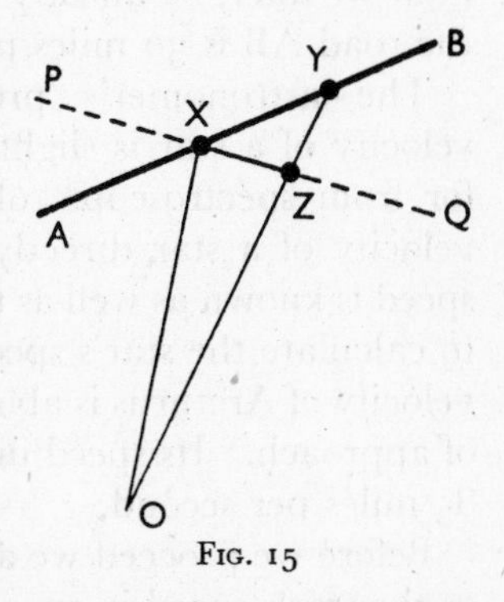

FIG. 15

actual speed along AB. We shall return to the last point in a little.

As an illustration of a star's transverse speed we consider the proper motion and distance of Arcturus, one of Halley's three stars. The proper motion is the large one of about $2\frac{1}{4}$ seconds of arc per annum or about $3\frac{3}{4}$ minutes of arc per century ; in the eighteen centuries between Hipparchus and Halley Arcturus has changed its position in the sky about $1\frac{1}{8}$ degrees. The distance of Arcturus is 40 light-years. From the proper motion and distance data it is calculated that the star's transverse speed is about 85 *miles per second*, that is, about 5000 times the speed of an express train.

Returning to Fig. 15 we remark that in one minute the motor-car, while moving from X to Y, has increased its distance from O by ZY : if we knew the distance ZY we should then be able to say that the rate at which the car was receding from us between X and Y is, say, 18 miles per hour ; this, in astronomical language, is known as the *radial velocity* and may be a velocity of recession, as in the case of the car in Fig. 15, or a velocity of approach under other circumstances. If our knowledge of the distance OX and the car's " proper motion " (1° per minute) is such that the transverse speed is 24 miles per hour we infer, by an easy calculation, that the car's speed along the road AB is 30 miles per hour.

The astronomer's procedure in calculating the space-velocity of a star is slightly different from the case of the car, for from spectroscopic observations he can derive the radial velocity of a star directly. Accordingly, when the transverse speed is known as well as the radial velocity, it is an easy matter to calculate the star's speed in space. For example, the radial velocity of Arcturus is about 3 miles per second and it is a speed of approach. Its speed in space, as defined, is thus a little over 85 miles per second.

Before we proceed we amplify what we have so far described as the star's speed in space. In the case of our motor-car illustration the observer at O is stationary and the speed of the car is related to fixed landmarks such as telephone poles on the road along which it is travelling. But space is not provided with fixed landmarks and when we say that the speed of Arcturus in space is a little over 85 miles per second we imply that this speed is relative to the Sun ; of course we make our observations from a fixed point on the surface of the Earth which is itself rotating about an axis and revolving around the Sun in its great orbit of 93 million miles radius with an average speed of $18\frac{1}{2}$ miles per second ; we can obviously make allowance for the observer's speed with reference to the Sun and accordingly we deduce the star's speed with reference to the Sun, just as if we were making the observations from our luminary.

This idea of motion relative to the Sun suggests at once a possible modification of our earlier statement that all the other stars are in motion. May it not be that it is the Sun alone that is moving in space and that the stars are immobile ? We can test this from the following considerations. In Fig. 16 let us suppose that the Sun moves from S to T in the course of a year and that this direction is exactly towards a star A. If X is a fixed star, comparatively near—say Arcturus—then the direction of X at the beginning of the year is along SX and at the end of the year it is along TX ; it is clear that, since the angle ATX is larger than the angle ASX, the star X will *appear* to be moving further from A in the sky—in other words the star X will be found to have a proper motion. Further, the star is nearer the Sun at the end of the year than it is at the beginning, and with spectroscopic equipment we should be able to measure, in this case, the radial velocity of approach. Suppose, for the moment, that we know the speed of the Sun along ST then, in the circumstances of the geometry of Fig. 16 (the distance of X from S, the angle which SX makes with SA) we can easily calculate both the proper motion and the radial velocity of the star X. Again, for all stars in the immediate neighbourhood of X these values of the proper motion and of the radial velocity should be substantially the same.

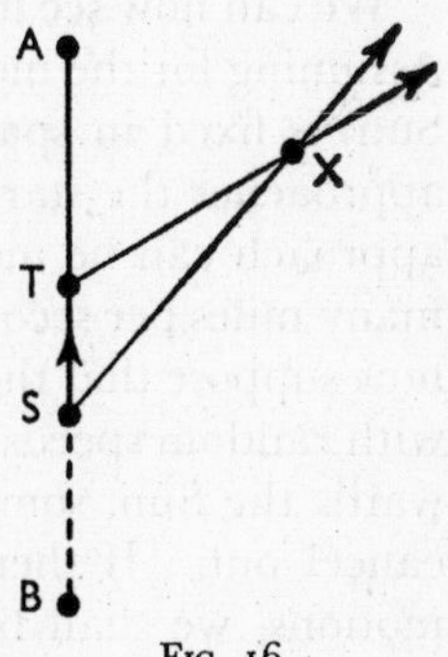

Fig. 16

What is the result of comparing these calculated proper motions and radial velocities with the corresponding observed values ? It is found that the observed proper motions as well as the radial velocities of a number of stars near X vary considerably from star to star, without any obvious connection between the individual values. On the other hand, if we take the *average* of the radial motions, for example, of say a hundred stars all at practically the same distance from the Sun and in the same part of the sky, the average does correspond to the calculated value of the radial velocity of these stars at or near X in Fig. 16. The same applies to the proper motions. It is evident then that the hypothesis of the fixity of the stars in space is untenable and we accordingly assume, in the first instance, that they are moving in space with random speeds and in random directions.

We can now see how the speed of the Sun can be determined. Assuming for the moment that the star A (directly ahead of the Sun) is fixed in space, then in the course of the year the Sun approaches the star by a distance ST and this radial speed of approach can be measured by means of the spectroscope as so many miles per second. Instead of a single fixed star at A let us now suppose that there are a hundred stars at or near A moving with random speeds ; some of these random motions will be towards the Sun, some away but on the whole they will tend to cancel out. If then we take the *average of the observed* radial motions, we shall be left substantially with the radial motion which we should have observed if each of the stars had been motionless in space ; in other words we measure the speed of the Sun in the direction SA.

In the same way, if B is a fixed star, directly behind the Sun, the observed speed of recession of B from the Sun is the same as the solar speed along ST and applying the argument to a hundred stars at or near B, each with its own random motion in space, we again obtain the solar speed from the average of the observed radial motions of these stars.

Consider now a *fixed* star at A ; the solar motion will have no effect in changing its position in the sky. Accordingly the observed proper motions of a hundred stars at or near A will arise from the random transverse speeds, some to the right of the line SA, some to the left and if we take any line perpendicular to SA, there will be some stars moving in one direction along this line and some in the opposite direction. We thus see that such proper motions will tend to cancel out and the average of the observed proper motions should be substantially zero. The same argument will apply to stars at or near B in Fig. 16. Further, the random transverse speeds of a number of stars near X will tend to cancel out and the average of the proper motions of such stars will be substantially that arising from the solar motion.

To find the point of the sky towards which the Sun is moving —this point is called the *solar apex*—we examine the proper motions of the stars in different sections of the sky and it is then possible to find two directions SA and the opposite direction SB such that the average proper motion is zero or nearly so. Having found these directions, the observations of radial velocities of stars at or near A and B will, on the average, lead to the actual rate at which the sun is moving along SA. This explains rather crudely how the position of the solar apex and the solar speed may be found ; in practice the astronomer makes use of all the available data of proper motions and radial velocities for the stars in whatever part of the sky they may be.

The first calculation of the position of the solar apex was made by Sir William Herschel from the observed proper motions of about a dozen stars. As the spectroscopic method of measuring radial velocities was not available effectively till almost a century after his time, he was unable to derive the solar speed. With the wealth of proper motion and radial velocity data now in our possession the solar motion is known with a considerable degree of exactitude and we state the result of such investigations : the Sun is moving with a speed of about 12 miles per second in a direction close to that of the bright star Vega—this speed is about 700 times the speed of an express train or several scores of times the speed of the fastest aeroplane.

When one reflects on the immense speeds of the stars the suggestion of the possibility of collisions between the stars immediately occurs. But the distance between any two stars is so enormous and the target which any single star presents is so small compared with these vast distances—for example, the distance between the Sun and its nearest stellar neighbour, Alpha Centauri, is about thirty million times the diameter of the Sun—that the probability of a stellar catastrophe in the shape of a collision is, according to calculations, infinitesimal even if we consider long periods of time of the order of a thousand million years. A collision is just as improbable as hitting a penny with a bullet at a range of a mile on a dark night when the direction of the penny is unknown.

We have taken the opportunity of describing some of the wider fields opened up by Halley's discovery of stellar proper motions. We now consider the details as they affect Sirius. We have previously remarked that the stars move in space in constant directions during the comparatively short intervals of time—say a century—during which their positions have been accurately observed ; this applies strictly to single stars. What happens in the case of a binary star ? In this case it is the centre of mass of the two components that moves in a constant direction ; each component describes an orbit with respect to this centre and if this point is moving in a straight line the component will appear to pursue a wavy kind of path with exact repetitions after each orbital period has been completed. Suppose that one of the components is so faint as to be invisible : in the sky the motion of the centre of mass will be represented by the broken line AB (Fig. 17) drawn with reference to the background of the stars ; but we cannot see the centre of mass, it is only the bright component we can observe. In the sky, then, the bright component will appear to move in the kind of wavy curve shown which is the result of a motion of revolution about a point which is itself moving in a straight line. It is of course to be understood that this curve is built up of observations of the position of the star, say, at yearly intervals. A simple analogy may make this clearer. Suppose a man and a girl are waltzing—we can suppose that each is revolving about a point halfway between them ; suppose further that their exertions carry them as a " system " in a straight line down the room. If the woman is in white and the man in black and the lights are so dim that the man is practically invisible the girl, being

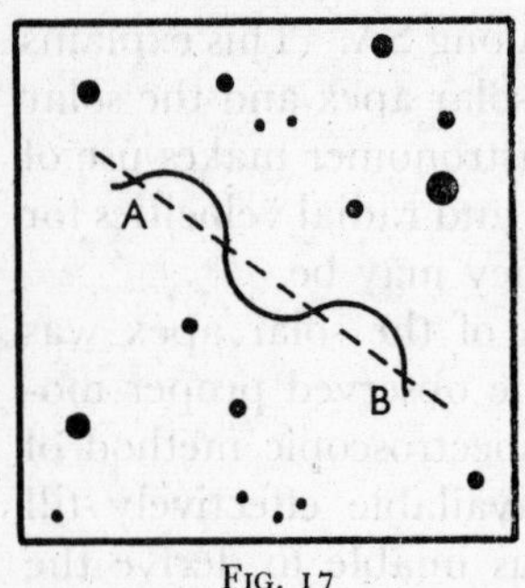

FIG. 17

visible, will be observed to pursue a path along the floor very much like the wavy line in Fig. 17.

In 1834 Bessel began to suspect that the bright star Sirius, which up to that time was seen in the telescope as a single star, pursued a path, against the background of the faint stars, which was not of the uniform sort represented by the broken line AB in Fig. 17. Observations in the following years turned sus-

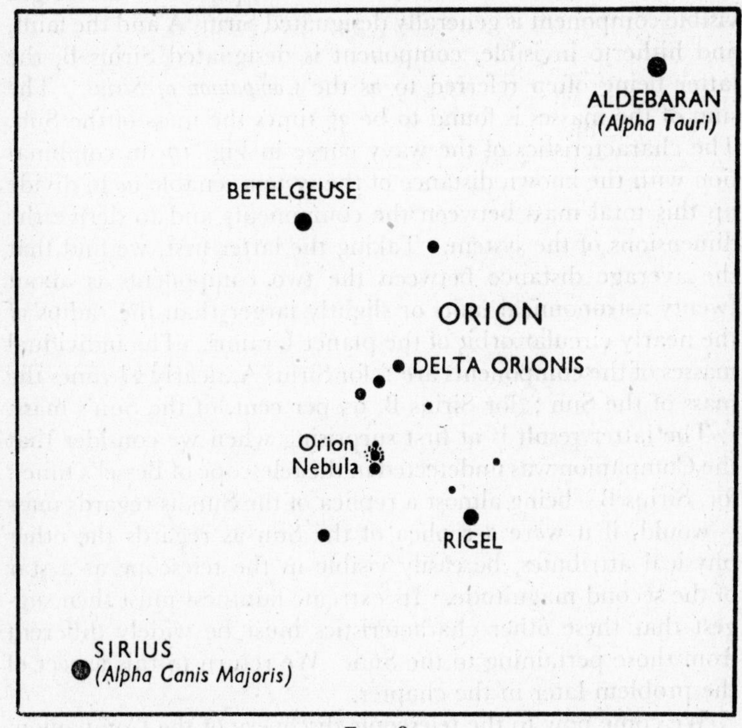

FIG. 18

picion into certainty ; the proper motion of the bright star Sirius was not uniform and the yearly positions of the star fitted on to a wavy curve of the form shown in Fig. 17. By 1844, just before his death, Bessel had concluded that Sirius must be a binary system, one component being too faint for detection in the telescope but sufficiently powerful, gravitationally, to show up the orbital motion of the bright component about the common centre of mass. Further, the observations, collected over many years, showed that the wavy curve was repeated at exact intervals in a period estimated by Bessel to be about fifty years —almost exactly equal to the result derived from more recent observations.

The position of Sirius is shown in the star-map in Fig. 18.

The known details of the binary system enable us to calculate the sum of the masses of the components—the bright visible component is generally designated Sirius A and the faint, and hitherto invisible, component is designated Sirius B, the latter being often referred to as the *Companion of Sirius*. The sum of the masses is found to be $3\frac{2}{5}$ times the mass of the Sun. The characteristics of the wavy curve in Fig. 17, in combination with the known distance of the system, enable us to divide up this total mass between the components and to derive the dimensions of the system. Taking the latter first, we find that the average distance between the two components is about twenty astronomical units or slightly larger than the radius of the nearly circular orbit of the planet Uranus. The individual masses of the components are : for Sirius A, nearly $2\frac{1}{2}$ times the mass of the Sun ; for Sirius B, 95 per cent. of the Sun's mass.

The latter result is at first surprising when we consider that the Companion was undetected in the telescope of Bessel's time ; for, Sirius B—being almost a replica of the Sun as regards mass —would, if it were a replica of the Sun as regards the other physical attributes, be easily visible in the telescope as a star of the second magnitude. Its extreme faintness must then suggest that these other characteristics must be widely different from those pertaining to the Sun. We return to this aspect of the problem later in the chapter.

We come now to the telescopic discovery of the Companion. From the observed data represented by the wavy curve in Fig. 17 it was possible to make predictions of the positions of the Companion relative to the bright orb of Sirius A. At the beginning of 1862 the celebrated American telescope-maker, Alvan Clark, was testing a new 20-inch lens—the biggest in those days—and turning the telescope on Sirius he saw a faint but unmistakeable point of light in almost the precise position predicted for 1862. The Companion was no longer merely a product, though unseen, of Bessel's genius ; now it was a visible reality.

Bessel is sometimes referred to as the founder of " the astronomy of the invisible ". We have just seen how his inferences as to the existence of a hitherto unseen companion of Sirius came triumphantly to fruition. He also predicted by the same method the binary character of the bright star Procyon, the companion of which—subsequently detected telescopically—has all the physical characteristics of Sirius B. Coming nearer home, Bessel was also amongst the first to be confident of the existence of a new planet beyond the orbit of Uranus, the most distant planet from the Sun then known and discovered by Sir William Herschel in 1781. About 40 years after its discovery and in subsequent years, the positions of Uranus in the sky deviated unmistakably from its predicted positions and in 1840 Bessel himself began to investigate the anomalous behaviour of Uranus with the firm conviction that the discrepancies referred to were the results of the attraction on Uranus of an unknown planet still more remote. Other preoccupations and failing health prevented much progress being made in converting his conviction into something more tangible. As is well known, the young Cambridge graduate J. C. Adams and the experienced French astronomer Le Verrier, independently and unknown to each other, attacked the problem successfully, and the planet—subsequently named Neptune—was discovered telescopically on 23rd September, 1846. This was perhaps one of the most sensational episodes in the history of Astronomy. One might speculate on the possibility of the association of Bessel's name uniquely with the discovery of Neptune had circumstances and health permitted, for there is little doubt that his genius would not have failed him in solving this most intricate problem ; in any event his proud title to be the founder of the astronomy of the invisible cannot be challenged.

Let us now consider in greater detail the information supplied by the observations of the binary Sirius. After the telescopic discovery in 1862, the orbit of the Companion as it appeared to circulate around the bright component was eventually derived ; this is shown in Fig. 19. The distance of Sirius is known with great accuracy ; it is one of the nearest stars to the Sun, its distance being 9 light-years. With this information the dimensions of the orbit can be easily deduced with results as previously stated. Further, the absolute magnitudes of the two components can be easily deduced from the apparent magnitudes. Now Sirius B is almost exactly 10 magnitudes fainter than Sirius A ; in other words, Sirius A is 10,000 times more luminous than the Companion. The absolute magni-

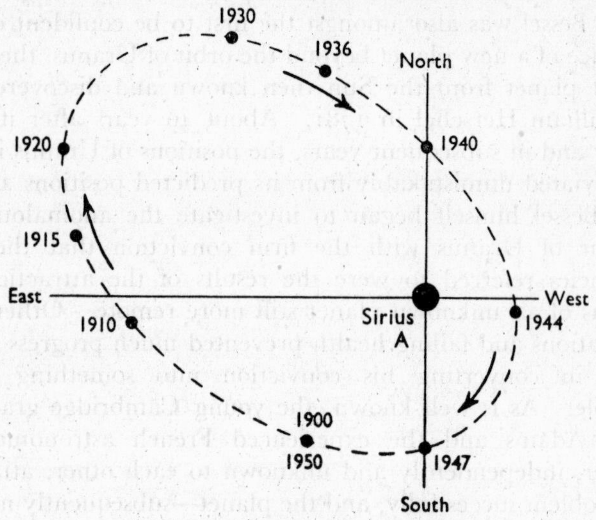

Fig. 19.—Orbit of Companion of Sirius

tudes of Sirius A and the Sun being known, it is deduced that Sirius A is about $35\frac{1}{2}$ times more luminous than the Sun and that the Sun is about 360 times more luminous than the Companion. Let us see what further deductions we can make from this information.

The luminosity of a star depends essentially on two factors. One factor is the temperature of its radiating surface (or photosphere), to which we refer succintly as the surface-temperature ; the higher the surface-temperature, the greater the star's candle-power or luminosity. The second factor is the surface area of the star—the larger the star, the greater is its total candle-power, or luminosity, It may be added that there is an exact physical law governing the relation between surface-temperature and the candle-power per unit of surface-area. We shall discuss later some of the principles which guide us to an estimate of the surface-temperature of a star ; meanwhile, we assume the results and apply them first to Sirius A.

It is found that the surface-temperatures of Sirius A and the Sun are such that the candle-power per square foot of the surface of Sirius A is about 15 times the candle-power per square foot of the surface of the Sun ; accordingly, if the dimensions of the two bodies were the same, the diversity of temperatures would lead to the result that the luminosity of Sirius A would be 15 times the Sun's luminosity. But we have seen that the luminosity of Sirius A is actually 35½ times the Sun's luminosity, from which we infer that the surface-area of Sirius A must be $35\frac{1}{2} \div 15$ or about $2\frac{2}{5}$ times the Sun's surface-area ; it then follows that the radius of Sirius A is a little more than $1\frac{1}{2}$ times the Sun's radius ; the latter radius is 432,000 miles and, accordingly, the radius of Sirius A is about 665,000 miles. It is in this way that, given the requisite observational material, we can obtain reliable estimates of the dimensions of many stars.

Let us now apply these principles to Sirius B. A reliable item of information is, as stated, that the Sun is about 360 times more luminous than the Companion and this would suggest that, in all probability, the Companion is smaller than the Sun and also, possibly, that its surface-temperature is lower than that of the Sun. For example, if its surface-temperature is half that of the Sun—it could hardly be very much less for, if so, the star would scarcely be luminous—the calculation shows that the Companion's radius would be about 90,000 miles, about one-fifth that of the Sun. If this were the star's actual radius, then, since its mass is just a little less than the Sun's mass, the average density of the stellar material must be nearly 150 times that of water, which would be regarded, even at the beginning of the century, as exceptionally high. If the surface-temperature were as low as 2500° C., corresponding to stars of deep red colour, the average density of the Companion would still be very high—about 50 times the density of water—and its radius would be about 130,000 miles. Now, for many years, it was found impossible to assign either colour or temperature to the Companion owing to the difficulty of seeing it, in the telescope, in the glare of its immensely more brilliant neighbour (Sirius A) ; astronomers were thus left with the presumption, based on the arguments relating to density, that the Companion must be considerably smaller than the Sun and that the feebleness of its radiating power must be ascribed to this circumstance together with low surface-temperature, the latter being the more important.

In 1915 Dr. W. S. Adams, of Mt. Wilson Observatory, succeeded in making the necessary observations from which the Companion's temperature could be obtained. In that year, as reference to Fig. 19 will show, the Companion was at a relatively large angular distance from Sirius A so that the interference of the glare of the bright component was as nearly as innocuous as it could be. Even so, the observations called for great technical skill. To his intense amazement Adams found that the Companion's surface-temperature was nearly half as large again as the Sun's, about 8000°, in fact. Instead of being a feebly radiating body as was supposed up to that time, Sirius B proved to be an intensely hot star radiating $3\frac{4}{5}$ times more heat and light energy per square foot than the Sun. Since the Sun is 360 times more luminous than the Companion it follows that the Sun's surface area must be $360 \times 3\frac{3}{4}$, or 1370, times the surface area of the Companion ; it is then easily deduced that the radius of the Companion is about 12,000 miles, just about three times the Earth's radius. The Companion is then of planetary dimensions with a radius about four-fifths that of Uranus, three-quarters that of Neptune, a third that of Saturn and two-sevenths that of Jupiter, the largest planet of all. Now we have seen that the mass of the Companion is just a little less than that of the Sun, the average density of the solar matter being $1\frac{2}{5}$ times that of water. The Sun, we recollect, is a globe of radius of 432,000 miles ; the Companion then turns out to be a body with a mass, practically equal to that of the Sun, compressed within a globe of but 12,000 miles radius. The average density of the Companion is easily calculated to be, in round figures, 65,000 times the density of water—an apparently fantastic result, and yet each step on the way to reaching it is certain and above suspicion. When a strange conclusion is reached in science, the first question that is asked is: Is there any way of confirming what seems so incredible a result by approaching the goal by another route? In due course the answer came from an unexpected quarter. Before we pass to the confirmation of the existence of matter in a state of enormous density we shall have to describe the application of spectroscopy to the stars.

In the first chapter we reflected that the only bridge between us and the visible universe was the light that reached us from the distant celestial bodies, and up to date we have been mainly concerned with the *direction* in which the light-rays travelled from a star to our eye. The fact that there is a variation in the colour of the stars immediately suggests that star-light, wherever it comes from, is not homogenous in its qualities; the spectroscope analyses the light and tells us what these qualities are. The main part of a spectroscope—or spectrograph, when photography is involved—consists of one or more prisms which perform the function of breaking up sunlight into the well-known rainbow colours, as we have already mentioned (page 24) in connection with Newton's famous discovery. When Wollaston, in 1802, using a spectroscope attached to the eye-end of a telescope, saw for the first time seven dark lines at right angles to the series of rainbow colours deriving from sunlight, the second great phase in the analysis of light was begun. With more powerful telescopes and spectroscopes the number of such dark lines—varying, it should be said, in intensity, some being more prominent and others barely visible—was increased very greatly; in 1814, Frauenhofer had counted no fewer than 574 lines deriving from sunlight and today the lines are counted in their thousands.

It is convenient here to introduce one or two technical terms. The series of rainbow colours is called the *continuous spectrum*; the dark lines are called *absorption lines*—it is just (although not quite) as if several fine sections of the complete continuous spectrum were blotted out or "absorbed" by something or other; the spectrum as a whole is called an *absorption spectrum*. When star-light was examined in a similar way it was seen that the absorption spectra varied very considerably.

The spectra of some stars showed a large number of absorption lines ; the spectra of others showed but a few. In several spectra an additional feature was observed—the presence of bright lines superimposed on the continuous spectrum ; such a spectrum is called an *emission spectrum.*

Progress in the interpretation of the characteristics of solar and stellar spectra became rapid when the groundwork had been firmly laid in the physical laboratory. In 1859, as a result of experiments, Kirchhoff formulated the three great laws of spectrum analysis which bear his name.

The first law states that incandescent solids (such as the filament of an electric-light bulb) and luminous gases under high pressure, produce a continuous spectrum.

The second law states that a luminous gas or vapour under low pressure produces a series of bright or emission lines ; for example hydrogen, at a very low pressure and made luminous by an electric discharge, shows a series of bright lines, one a red line and others with colours ranging up to the violet end of the spectrum ; sodium vapour, produced easily by holding in a bunsen flame a platinum wire, on which a small amount of salt is placed, produces two vivid yellow lines close together ; and so on for other elements, each having its own characteristic series of emission lines, varying from element to element in number, intensity and position in the spectrum.

The third law can be illustrated by the experiment of shining the light from an electric bulb *through* the vapour of sodium produced in the bunsen flame as already described ; the spectrum now consists of the full range of the rainbow colours (the continuous spectrum produced by the filament, according to the first law) and two close *dark* lines in the yellow part of the spectrum, exactly in the same positions as the pair of emission lines produced by sodium vapour according to the second law. It is a fair inference to suggest that the atoms of sodium in the experiment have the peculiar property of absorbing part, at least, of the corresponding portions of the continuous spectrum produced by the filament. It may be stated at once that it is only *part* of the yellow light of the continuous spectrum that is absorbed in this way, for although the lines appear dark and " light-less " they do so only by contrast against the adjacent brilliant spectrum ; there is, in fact a certain amount of light emanating from the apparently dark lines.

Let us first apply these laws to the spectrum of the Sun ; it consists of a continuous spectrum crossed by an immense number of dark or absorption lines. Applying the first law we conclude that the continuous spectrum is produced by luminous gases at high pressure and the rather undefinable surface where this density is sufficiently great is called the *photosphere*, shown in Fig. 20 ; above the photosphere there is a shell of luminous gases and vapours, of rapidly diminishing density and temperature, called the *reversing-layer* ; above this again is the thin atmosphere known as the *chromosphere*. Suppose that in the reversing-layer there are atoms of sodium ; the intense light from the photosphere passes through this cooler cloud of atoms and by the third law we should expect that part of the photospheric radiation—that is, part of the continuous spectrum—will be absorbed by the sodium atoms thereby producing a close pair of dark or absorption lines in the yellow part of the spectrum.

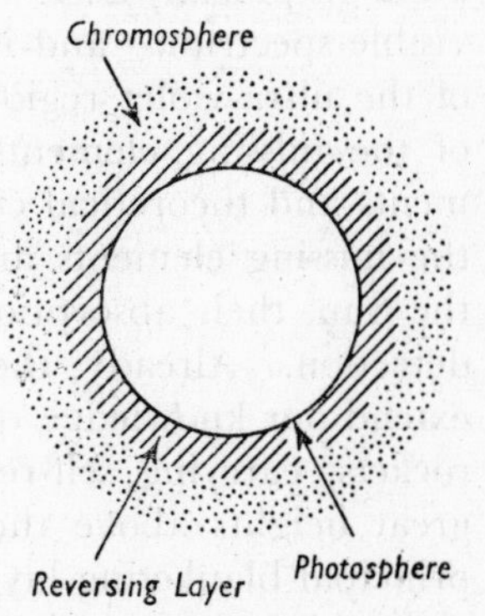

FIG. 20

We now examine the solar spectrum (see Plate IV (a), facing page 49) and there we see a close pair of absorption lines—called by Frauenhofer the D lines—exactly where we should expect to find them. The inference is, of course, that the sodium atoms are present in the Sun's reversing layer. From laboratory experiments it is known that iron vapour (made luminous by an intense electrical stimulation) produces hundreds of bright lines ; each of these can be matched in the solar spectrum with an absorption line ; we infer again that iron is a constituent of the Sun's reversing layer. It is in this way that we can deduce that about sixty out of the 92 known terrestrial elements are constituents of our luminary.

It may be asked : Are the remaining elements not present in the Sun ? Let us first consider the visible spectrum—that is, the range of colours which we can actually *see* with the eye—and, second, the range of spectrum that can be photographed. The two ranges are not the same, for the capacity of the eye to record the radiations from the Sun is different from the capacity of the photographic plate. The ordinary plate is much more sensitive than the eye for radiations beyond the visible violet end—this extension revealed by the plate (and beyond) is known as the *ultra-violet.* Again, certain types of plates are sensitive to radiations beyond the red end of the spectrum visible to the eye—this extension is known as the *infra-red.* But owing to the blanketing capacity of the Earth's atmosphere there is only a comparatively small part of the ultra-violet photographically accessible—contiguous to the violet end of the visible spectrum—and it is in the normally unobservable part of the ultra-violet region that the lines characteristic of most of the missing elements are known from laboratory experiments and theoretical considerations to lie. Again, if some of the missing elements are really in extremely short supply in the Sun, their absorption lines would be so faint as to escape detection. Already, there have been successful attempts * to extend our knowledge of the solar spectrum made by sending rockets, carrying self-registering spectroscopic equipment, to great heights above the Earth's surface and well above the principal blanketing layers of the atmosphere.

At this point we must say something more explicitly about the method of identifying lines in the solar and stellar spectra with particular elements. We are familiar with waves propagated on the surface of a pond ; the distance between two successive crests is called the *wave-length*, and this varies according to the degree of disturbance caused by, say, dropping a stone on the placid surface of the water. On the electromagnetic theory of light we suppose, in a similar way, that light is propagated by a wave-motion and with each element of the continuous spectrum is associated a particular wave-length. In the laboratory the wave-lengths of each of the pair of emission lines produced by sodium can be found with high accuracy ;

* The earliest, near the end of 1946, made with a German V2 rocket, recorded the ultra-violet spectrum of the Sun as far as 2200 Angstrom units (for definition of this unit see page 77).

these wave-lengths are so excessively minute that it is found convenient to introduce a special unit—called the *Angstrom unit* (denoted by A) after one of the pioneers of spectroscopy. If a centimetre (about two-fifths of an inch) is divided into a hundred million equal parts, the length of one of these parts is the Angstrom unit. It is found, for example, that the wave-lengths of the two sodium D lines are 5890·186 A and 5896·35 A.

In the same way, the wave-lengths of the multitude of iron lines are found.

In investigating the spectrum of the Sun or a star one common procedure is to photograph, alongside the solar or stellar spectrum, the spectrum of luminous iron vapour (or some other element or elements) the lines of which, with their known wave-lengths, form a series of standards by which the wave-length of any line in the solar or stellar spectrum can be deduced from accurate measurement. For example, if the wave-length of a particular absorption line in the solar spectrum is deduced, by the method indicated, to be 4226·9 A we can infer from the known laboratory wave-lengths of magnesium that this line in the solar spectrum betrays the presence of magnesium in the Sun. The reader is referred to Plate IV, facing page 49, where the stellar spectra are shown flanked by comparison spectra above and below.

The study of spectra enables us, further, to learn a great deal about the physical states of the outer atmospheres of the stars and, in particular, the temperatures of their photospheres, or radiating surfaces, to which we refer simply as the surface-temperatures. The estimation of temperature is, in reality, a difficult process and we give here only a slight indication of one or two methods of attack. It is well known that chemical compounds dissociate into their constituent elements by the application of heat ; some break up at moderate temperatures, but others show considerable resistance to dismemberment. In the cooler stars certain compounds reveal their presence by imprinting one or more close series of lines—or bands—on the spectrum and in such stars we deduce that the temperature is not greater than that required for dissociation. Here is one clue to the study of stellar temperatures.

Another clue is found in the relative intensities of the different sections of the continuous spectrum which, when correlated with known physical principles, provides an estimate of temperature. Red stars appear red because the most intense part of the light radiated by the star comes from the red end of the spectrum, with diminishing intensity in the other colours and with amost negligible intensity from the violet or blue end. In the same way a blue star has the greatest light intensity in the blue part of the spectrum with feeble intensity at the red end. These are virtually the extremes, with yellow and white stars as intermediates. There is then a progression in temperature on passing from red to blue stars, the latter being hotter than the former, so far as their radiating surfaces are concerned.

The elements are themselves dissociated under suitable conditions of temperature and pressure, and this brings us by a series of steps to the understanding as to how matter can attain the exceedingly high density which we have deduced for the Companion of Sirius. We consider some aspects of atomic structure necessary for our immediate purpose.

The fundamental particles of which the atoms of the elements are built up are protons, electrons and neutrons. Each atom consists of a *nucleus* which carries a positive charge of electricity and around it circulate, like planets revolving around the Sun, a number of electrons—the number varies according to the element in its normal state—each of which carries a unit charge of negative electricity, the total number of such units exactly counterbalancing the positive charge on the nucleus.

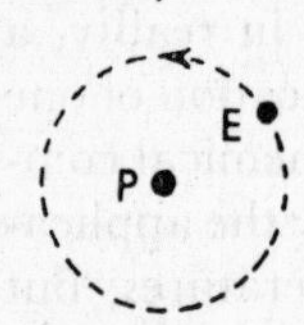

FIG. 21.—Hydrogen Atom

The hydrogen atom is the simplest of these atomic structures ; its nucleus consists of a single positively charged particle to which the special name of *proton* has been given and around the nucleus revolves a single electron. Fig. 21 represents the hydrogen atom, the proton being denoted by P and the electron by E. It is found that the mass of a proton is about 1840 times that of an electron and consequently the mass of the hydrogen atom is almost entirely concentrated in its nucleus.

The helium atom comes next in simplicity of structure ; its nucleus consists of a compact entity built up of two protons and two neutrons; the mass of the neutron, which is an uncharged particle, is practically that of the proton; around the nucleus of the helium atom circulate *two* electrons, the two negative units counter-balancing the positive charges on the two protons of the nucleus. The model of the helium atom is represented in Fig. 22 in which N denotes the nucleus. As we proceed through the series of elements, the number of planetary electrons increases and the nuclei become more and more complicated structures; the heaviest element of all is uranium, the nucleus of which consists of 92 protons and 146 neutrons, and around it circulate 92 electrons.

The atom is sometimes likened to the solar system, the electrons taking the part of the planets and the nucleus that of the Sun. In the solar system, however, the Sun is the controlling body by reason of its immense gravitational attraction on the individual planets, whereas in the atom the control of the nucleus on the planetary electrons is expressed in terms of the electrical attraction between positively and negatively charged particles. Just as the dimensions of the solar system are immense compared with the dimensions of the Sun and the individual planets, so too is the atom, as a structure, immensely greater than its component nucleus and electrons. If we consider the hydrogen atom, for example, the radius of the normal orbit of the circulating electron is about 25,000 times greater than the radius of the electron which itself is about 200 times the radius of the nuclear proton. Similar considerations apply to the atoms of the other elements; all are systems immensely larger than their component parts.

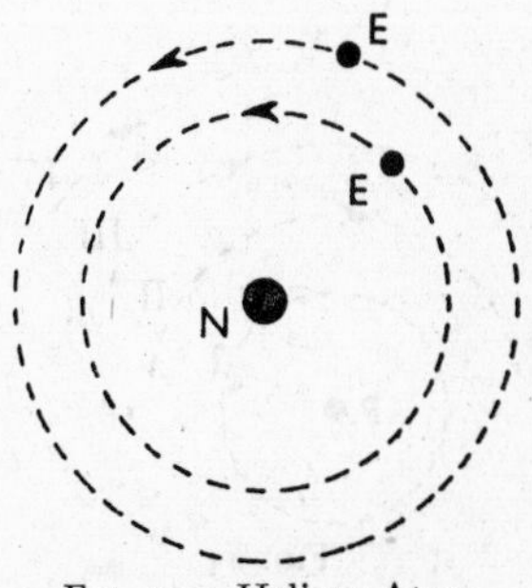

FIG. 22.—Helium Atom

The mechanism by which an atom radiates energy in the form of light and heat and absorbs radiation may be briefly illustrated in the case of the hydrogen atom—we take the conclusions of physics as our basis. The single electron of the hydrogen atom is not free to revolve about the nucleus in *any* orbit; the choice is, in fact, hedged about with precise rules.

In Fig. 23 the orbit denoted by I is that occupied by the electron when it is incapable of emitting radiation in any form and, for purposes of reference, we can say it is the normal orbit. The radii of the next orbits—II, III, IV and so on—are respectively 4, 9, 16 times the radius of I (these are not shown in Fig. 23 according to the correct scale).

Suppose that a hydrogen atom finds itself in its normal state in the solar atmosphere ; it is exposed to the intense radiation coming from the layers below and it has the capacity to absorb a part of this radiation provided it is of one or other of certain discrete wave-lengths. The effect of absorption of this *quantum* of radiation, as it is called, is the immediate "jump" of the electron to a higher orbit, say III ; the atom has thus acquired more energy than it had in its normal state and it proceeds at once to get rid of some of it by "jumping" back to orbit II, say. The release of energy takes the form of a pulse of light of a particular wave-length—in this instance the conspicuous red line in the emission spectrum of hydrogen. It is to be noted, too, that the emission of this particular light may be in *any* direction in space. The effect of the double operation, first, of the absorption of the photospheric radiation and, second, the discharge of the radiation corresponding to the red light of hydrogen in a direction with little chance of being *towards* us, is to weaken the continuous spectrum precisely at the wave-length of the red line ; consequently, we shall have a diminution of light at this particular wave-length —in other words, we shall have an absorption line there.

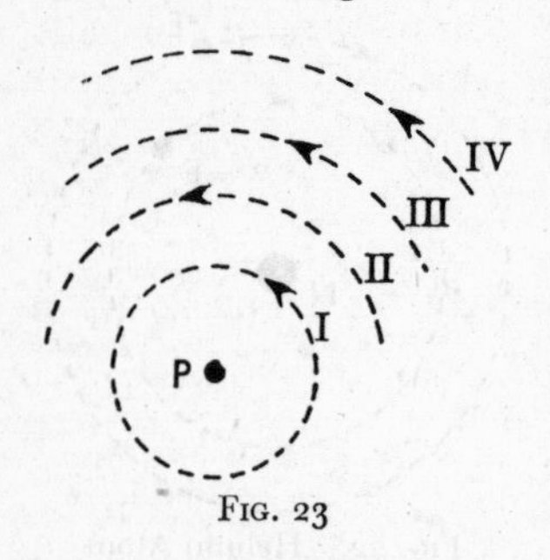

FIG. 23

We have considered one "transition", as it is called, but it is evident that the number of possible transitions is very great. Further, the bigger the quantum of energy which the atom absorbs the greater is the radius of the orbit to which the electron jumps ; if the quantum exceeds a certain calculable amount the electron will be shot out beyond the control of the nucleus ; the atomic structure will be broken up and instead of having a complete hydrogen atom with which we started we shall be left with two independent particles, one a proton, and the other an electron.

Now, consider briefly a lithium atom (Fig. 24) consisting of a nucleus N (built up of three protons and four neutrons) and three planetary electrons, E, F and G. The normal spectrum of lithium is associated with the "jumps" of the outermost electron G. Suppose that the absorption of radiation is such as to drive the electron G beyond the control of the nucleus; the atom is now reduced to the nucleus (still with three positive charges, since there are three protons embedded in it) together with two planetary electrons; the disrupted atom as a whole is positively charged and having lost one electron it is referred to as a *singly-ionised* atom. If the radiation is sufficiently intense the second electron F may be expelled and the atom, now having lost two electrons and consisting of the nucleus and the remaining electron E, is said to be doubly-ionised. If the radiation is still more intense, the electron E may be finally parted from the nucleus; the atom is then completely ionised. Thus, starting with a structure of some complexity, we see that it is possible to finish up with four independent particles, namely, a nucleus and three electrons.

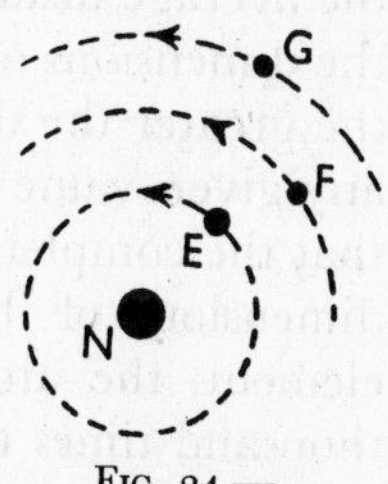

Fig. 24.—Lithium Atom

Atoms can also be ionised by means of collisions, one or more of the outermost electrons of one atom being torn off as the result of rough handling by a second atom. It is necessary to add that the spectra associated with an undamaged atom and with any of its ionised forms (singly, doubly, etc.) are all different. It may be that the spectra of one or more of the ionised forms of a particular element are in the unobservable part of the ultra-violet and, consequently, if the conditions in the star are such as to be effective in ionising all the atoms of the element to the degree concerned, then the stellar spectrum will furnish no evidence as to the presence of that element in the star. The non-detection of some of the elements in the Sun and also in the stars is accounted for in this way.

The phenomenon of ionisation provides the clue to the interpretation of the high density in the Sun and the stars, the solar and stellar material being still regarded as gaseous. The peculiar characteristic of a gas is the large separation on the average between any two neighbouring atoms or molecules ; for this reason the gas can be compressed even up to the limit when the atoms or molecules are jammed tightly together, this stage corresponding to liquefaction or solidification. To complete the picture of a gas we add that the atoms or molecules are rushing about in all sorts of directions with all sorts of speeds colliding with one another and with the inner surface of the containing vessel, very much like half a dozen balls moving at random on the surface of a billiard table, colliding on occasions with one another or impinging on the cushions of the table.

The degree of compressibility of a gas is evidently related to the average distance between a pair of atoms or molecules and the dimensions of the latter ; the smaller the atom or molecule the greater the degree to which the gas can be compressed for any given value of this average distance. Now, we have seen that the complete atom is a bulky structure compared with the dimensions of its nucleus and an electron ; for an average element, the atomic diameter is of the order of a hundred thousand times the diameter of the nucleus.

In the extreme case of the complete ionisation of the atoms, the original bulky atoms are now replaced by particles—nuclei and electrons—of dimensions only a minute fraction of the atomic dimensions and, consequently, considerable compression, resulting in a great increase in density, appears to be possible. Near the centre of the Sun the density of the material may be fifty times that of water but if this material consists mainly of the debris of broken-down atoms (from which perhaps a large proportion of planetary electrons may have been torn away) its gaseous state is not in question. Moreover, there is still the possibility of further severe compression beyond that encountered in normal dwarf stars such as the Sun, provided that the ionisation of the atoms is still more thorough. This is the state to which the Companion of Sirius is reduced—and to even a greater degree in the case of one or two white dwarfs in which the density is estimated to be as much as ten times that of the Companion. Matter in this extremely dense state is referred to as a "degenerate gas" in which the electrical attractions between oppositely charged particles and the repulsions between particles carrying similar electrical charges introduce complications unknown in such a gas as the terrestrial atmosphere in which these electrical attractions and repulsions are absent.

Earlier in the chapter we have referred to the astonishment with which astronomers in 1915 greeted the inference from Adams' spectroscopic observations of the Companion, namely, that here we had a star of incredibly immense density. Some years before our ideas on the processes of ionisation had been consolidated and before the apparently simple solution of the problem associated with the existence of supra-dense matter in the universe had been put forward—as described in the preceding pages—Adams had obtained, in 1924, observations of a wholly different character which removed any lingering doubt concerning the high density of the Companion. The observations had as their first object the measurement of the wave-lengths of absorption lines in the spectrum of the Companion. As we have seen the Companion is ten magnitudes fainter than the brilliant component Sirius A, and the photography of the Companion's spectrum in the glare of the bright star bristled with difficulties that seemed insuperable. Nevertheless, Adams achieved the almost impossible. His main measurements were concerned with the wave-length of one of the hydrogen absorption lines in the Companion's spectrum.

Now, as we have indicated earlier, the presence of a particular element in the Sun or in a star is inferred from the identity of the wave-lengths of absorption lines in the solar or stellar spectrum, characteristic of the particular element, with the wave-lengths of the corresponding lines in laboratory spectra. Actually, the wave-lengths in the two cases are not *precisely* identical, as a rule, owing to various circumstances two of which are relevant in the present connection.

In the first place, if a star has a radial velocity of recession, all the lines in the stellar spectrum will be displaced by comparatively minute amounts towards the red end of the spectrum so that their wave-lengths will be measured slightly larger than the corresponding laboratory wave-lengths; if the radial velocity is one of approach the displacements will be towards the violet end of the spectrum with a slight diminution in wave-lengths as compared with the laboratory wave-lengths. We deal with the particular feature of spectroscopic observations in greater detail in the following chapter, but, meanwhile, we shall be content to state that the measurement of the displacement of absorption lines enables us to calculate, in miles per second, the radial velocity of approach, or of recession, of the star (see Plate IV (b), facing page 49, in which the displacement of the absorption lines is clearly visible). Conversely, if we know the radial velocity we can calculate the displacement of any particular line.

Consider now the binary system of Sirius for which we know the dimensions of the system, the masses of each component and the orientation of the system in space. We can readily calculate the circumstances of motion of each component about the centre of mass of the system and, in particular, the contribution (expressed in terms of radial velocity) of each component; it is convenient to refer to this contribution as the " orbital radial velocity ". The displacement of the lines in a spectrum of Sirius A—which is easily photographed—will yield the *observed* radial velocity of the star and this will be compounded of the orbital radial velocity and the radial velocity of the system as a whole or, expressed otherwise, of the centre of mass. The first part of the observed radial velocity being obtained by calculation, as indicated, the radial velocity of the centre of mass can now be found.

Consider now the Companion ; since the orbital radial velocity is known from the calculation alluded to and the radial velocity of the centre of mass of the system has just been found, the combined result should be consistent with the observed displacement of the absorption lines in the Companion's spectrum, provided that there is no other phenomenon involved. Adams found that there was a displacement towards the red end of the spectrum still outstanding and amounting, in terms of radial velocity, to $12\frac{1}{2}$ miles per second. Clearly, some other factor must be operating strongly to produce such a discrepancy.

This factor—the second of the two which we mentioned as relevant—was predicted quantitatively by Einstein in his theory of relativity. We explain the effect in the following general terms. A quantum of radiation of a particular wave-length emitted outwards at the Sun's surface starts off with a certain amount of energy part of which it gives up in escaping from the gravitational control of the Sun ; in consequence, according to physical principles, the wave-length is somewhat increased. Taking all such quanta into account we have a displacement of all parts of the spectrum—and including absorption lines—towards the red end. The magnitude of this displacement varies directly with the Sun's mass and inversely as the Sun's radius. In the case of the Sun the displacement is hardly detectable, mainly because of the comparatively large radius of the Sun.

But in the case of the Companion, with practically the same mass as the Sun but with a radius only one thirty-sixth part of the solar radius, the displacement of any line is 36 times larger than for the Sun and, when calculated by the appropriate formula and then expressed in terms of radial velocity, it is found to be equivalent to 12 miles per second—almost precisely the result derived from Adams' observations. This striking confirmation can leave us in no doubt that in the Companion of Sirius we have a celestial body with the immense density we have earlier deduced.

Because of its colour and feeble luminosity and size the Companion is described as a *White Dwarf*. Several other White Dwarfs are known and as these stars are all amongst the Sun's nearest neighbours it would seem that White Dwarfs form a significant proportion of the stellar population.

Chapter IV

ALGOL, THE DEMON STAR

The term " fixed stars " implies that the configuration of the constellations remained constant from year to year and from century to century ; Halley's discovery of proper motion, as we have seen, dispelled once and for all this conception of a static universe. The term was also generally taken to imply that the stars appeared to be unchanging in brightness, and like the first this conception in due course received its quietus. It is true that a few " new " stars, or *novae*, had been noticed—the earliest the nova observed by Hipparchus in 134 B.C.—and they had no doubt given even the early astronomers an incentive to speculate on what these stars are, how they come into such spectacular prominence, and why they disappear from sight after a brief reign in the sky.

But except for these occasional and mysterious occurrences there appeared to be amongst astronomers no suspicion of any variability of the brightness of the stars—even of modest extent as compared with the startling changes shown by a " new " star—until the year 1596, when David Fabricius, an amateur astronomer, noticed that a third magnitude star in the constellation of the Whale (Cetus) was no longer visible in October of that year. It is to be remembered that this was before the invention of the telescope in 1609. The star had evidently reappeared, for in 1603 Bayer—who it will be recollected " named " the brightest stars in each constellation by giving them Greek letters—assigned the Greek letter Omicron to the star. In 1638-39 Omicron Ceti, for such is its professional name, was observed by a Dutch astronomer to pass through a cycle of changes in brightness, the period of which was found some years later to be about 334 days. The phenomenon, unique at the time, appeared so remarkable that the star received the epithet " Mira "—the " wonderful "—by which name it is familiarly known even to this day.

In the previous chapters we have referred to the only bridge between us and the stars, namely, star-light ; we have utilised the observations of the direction in which the rays of light reach us to specify the positions of the stars in the sky and to deduce their distances and their proper motions ; we have investigated —to some extent—the quality or physical properties of the light emitted by the stars to find out their chemical constitutions and temperatures ; in this chapter we are to be concerned with the *changes* in the quantity of light reaching us from a particular star. A star, such as Mira Ceti, which changes in brightness is called a *Variable star* or simply a *Variable*.

There are several distinct types of variable depending on the cause of the light-variation ; a nova, for example, is classed as a variable and here the changes in brightness occur on a catastrophic scale, just as if the star had suddenly exploded ; Mira Ceti belongs to another type where the changes in brightness can be traced to periodic happenings in a single star ; the theme of the present chapter is the class of variables known as " eclipsing binaries " and the best-known star of this type is *Algol* or Beta Persei, known as the *Demon Star* and up to the eighteenth century occasionally as the star in the head of Medusa.

The position of Algol is shown in the star-map in Fig. 25.

The name Algol is the corrupted form of the Arabian name El Ghoul, which means, according to the authorities, " changing spirit ", from which the name " Demon Star " is derived. Why was this star so called by the Arabs and what were the suggestive features that found expression in its name ? It would seem to be more than probable that the Arabs discovered that Algol fluctuated noticeably in brightness, no doubt ascribing the mysterious changes to supernatural agencies, and that, in fact, in our phraseology Algol was recognised by them as a variable star. It may be added that we have the authority of Dr. Z. Kopal, one of the leading experts on variable stars, for stating that the Hebrews knew the star as " Satan's Head " and that the Chinese called it " Piled-up Corpses " ! It is not easy to see any connection between either of these picturesque names and the phenomenon of light-changes associated with Algol, and we must conclude—perhaps regretfully—that the star's variability was undetected or unknown to Hebrews and Chinese alike.

Coming to less remote times we find that light-changes in Algol were noticed by Montanari in November 1670 and again in 1733 by Miraldi ; but evidently little attention was paid to what must have seemed a rather peculiar star and certainly no authentic observations of a systematic nature were made by anyone until 1782 when a significant discovery was made by a youth, John Goodricke of York, who was born at Groningen

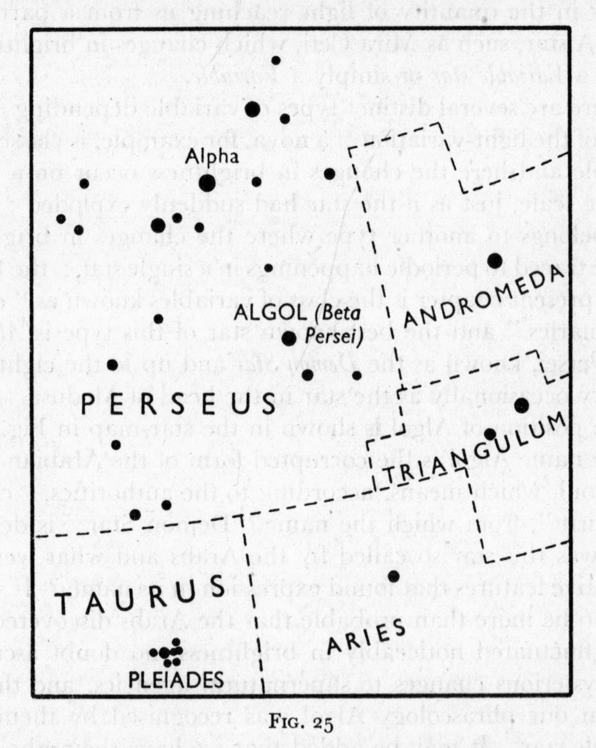

Fig. 25

in Holland in 1764. Heir to a baronetcy and destined to die at the early age of twenty-one and a half years, Goodricke suffered from the double disability of being deaf and dumb, and no doubt as a result of these physical infirmities he had leisure and opportunity to become absorbed in the study of the night-sky. On the evening of 12th November, 1782, Goodricke noticed that Algol was becoming fainter and, continuing his observations, he further noticed that after being—as we know

now—only one-third as bright as it normally was, the star began to brighten up again to its former brightness.

When the star is at its faintest, it is said to be at minimum brightness. To illustrate the sequence of changes we shall refer to a modern *light-curve*, as it is called, leaving out for the present several details which have their own significance but are superfluous in relation to Goodricke's discovery. We shall suppose that the magnitude of Algol can be measured at any time say with reference to a neighbouring star, of comparable brightness and of known magnitude, which is assumed to be unvarying.

We then plot the magnitude of Algol against the time, say, at ten-minute intervals when such small intervals are necessary,

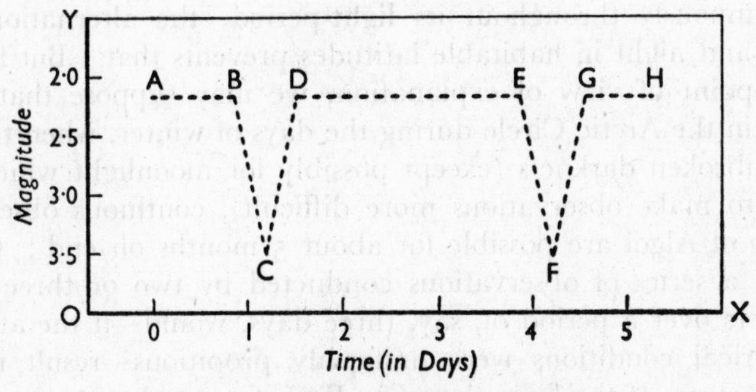

FIG. 26.—Crude Light-Curve of Algol

or at less frequent intervals when the star's brightness is not fluctuating. We shall find that over a series of considerable intervals the star will be of constant brightness, as shown over the stretches AB, DE and GH in Fig. 26 in which a dot is intended to represent an observation consisting of the appropriate magnitude measurement at a particular time. Then, starting at the point B, the star will be observed for five hours to become fainter and fainter and this will be represented by the part BC of the diagram ; at C the star is of minimum brightness and is then giving out only about one-third of the light which it emits when its magnitude is represented by any point on AB. Immediately after minimum at C, the star increases in brightness and within five hours it regains the brightness it had just previous to its fading. For about 2 days and 11 hours it maintains this brightness and this stretch is represented by DE in the figure. At the expiry of this time the process of first fading away in 5 hours and then recapturing its original brightness in 5 hours more is repeated exactly ; this is represented by EF and FG, and F is the corresponding minimum. The cycle of changes proceeds with the regularity of a clock. The interval between two successive minima such as C and F is called the period of the light-changes and is evidently connected intimately with some property or some set of circumstances peculiar to the star. The curve such as is represented in Fig. 26 is the *light-curve* and the study of the light-curve enables us to make certain deductions to which we refer later.

It is not to be supposed that Algol can normally be observed continuously throughout its light-period—the alternation of day and night in habitable latitudes prevents that. But from the point of view of explanation, we may suppose that far within the Arctic Circle during the days of winter, when there is unbroken darkness (except possibly for moonlight which is apt to make observations more difficult), continous observations of Algol are possible for about 5 months on end ; then such a series of observations conducted by two or three observers over a period of, say, three days, would—if the atmospherical conditions were uniformly propitious—result in a light-curve of the form shown in Fig. 26 ; a subsequent series of such observations would, of course, result in the reproduction of the light-curve. In actual practice, at an established observatory, only a small part of the light-curve—corresponding to observations over perhaps an interval of four or five hours—is the fruit of one night's labours ; but once the period of light-variation is known—and this is generally found easily and accurately from observations extending over a few months—all the observations, whenever made, can be represented in a light-curve just as if they had all been made by our Arctic observers within a period of three days.

John Goodricke's observations on the night of 12th November, 1782, were observations of Algol before and after the time at which minimum occurred ; and in terms of Fig. 26 we may say that, without making estimates of magnitude, he was aware of the diminution of brightness between B and C and the subsequent gradual brightening after the minimum, at C, was passed. What he did observe as accurately as his means would allow was the time of minimum. He continued his observations throughout the winter observing such minima as were possible—some of course occurred during day-light hours and so escaped observation—and in a short time he was able to deduce the period of light-changes, that is, the true interval between C and F in Fig. 26. His final estimate for the period was 2 days 20 hours 49 minutes 8 seconds, an amazingly accurate result when judged even by modern standards. He communicated his discovery to the Royal Society in May 1783 in a paper with the informative title " A series of observations on, and a discovery of, the period of the variation of the light of the bright star in the Head of Medusa, called Algol ", and a later one in which he discussed further the phenomenon of light-variation.

At the conclusion of his first paper Goodricke suggested that the cause of the phenomenon was the periodic eclipse of Algol by a large and dark body—essentially of stellar dimensions and possibly only faintly luminous—revolving about Algol in the same period as that of the light-changes. This explanation apparently did not commend itself at first to Sir William Herschel, then at the height of his fame, for, as he said, he had repeatedly observed Algol with his 7-foot telescope and found it " distinctly single ". It was later Herschel's good fortune to discover the existence of binary stars (*v.* page 38) and he was now disposed to accept the binary character of Algol, although he was still unable to detect the hypothetical companion in his telescope.

As we now know, the reason for his failure is not far to seek. Consider two well-known binaries of the type Herschel observed, Sirius (the principal theme of the previous chapter) and Alpha Centauri, our nearest stellar neighbour ; the average distance between the components of Sirius is a little over 20 astronomical units or 190 million miles, while the average separation of the components of Alpha Centauri is 217 million miles. In the telescope the components of each binary appear fairly near one another but, if the linear distance between the components of Sirius or Alpha Centauri were only one per cent.

of the actual distance, it is almost entirely certain that the largest telescope so far constructed would be powerless to show them separated in the field of view. When it is stated that the distance between the two components of Algol—for Goodricke's surmise was later confirmed—is on the average but 6 million miles, it is then not surprising that Herschel failed to detect the faint companion.

Before proceeding to discuss the kind of information which a light-curve can furnish we shall first describe some of the principal methods for measuring the light-changes of a variable. If the star is faint, the star-field in which the variable is situated is photographed in the usual way ; each star records its image on the plate, the size of the image bearing a definite relationship to the star's brightness ; the relationship can be found from theoretical considerations applied to a special and elaborate technique which we need not explain. We can then suppose that we can derive the magnitude of each star.

In the field of view, then, we select say half a dozen stars, which we call reference stars, the brightest of which—call it A —is a little brighter than the variable when the latter's brightness is greatest, and the faintest—call it F—is just a little fainter than the variable at minimum. At whatever time the variable is observed photographically, its magnitude will lie within the range of magnitudes of A and F.

Measuring the diameters of the images of the six reference stars and the diameter of the image of the variable, we have then six ways of calculating the magnitude of the variable and we take the average thereby hoping to increase the accuracy of the determination. When a series of photographs are taken at intervals, we can then deduce the particular points on the light-curve to which the individual observations refer. These photographs need not be taken on separate plates ; the same plate will suffice for a considerable number of exposures for, by sliding the plate-holder—say, a tenth of an inch to the right for each of successive exposures—we obtain a series of images as illustrated in Fig. 27. If the exposures are all of the same duration, then the individual images of star A will be substantially the same in size ; similarly, for stars B to F. If the observer is fortunate enough to obtain a series of exposures such that the middle one is made at or near principal minimum of the variable the series of images will resemble the series illustrated in Fig. 27 at V. The photographic observations can then be used to fill in gaps of, or add improvements to, the light-curve which in this case is concerned with photographic magnitudes.

When a faint star is observed visually, the observer's first concern is to assign magnitudes to several reference stars chosen in the same way as for photographic observations. His procedure is then to estimate the visual magnitude of the variable by means of the reference stars. A great amount of valuable observations, especially of the fainter variables, has been, and is being, done by amateur astronomers in all parts of the world with comparatively modest equipment.

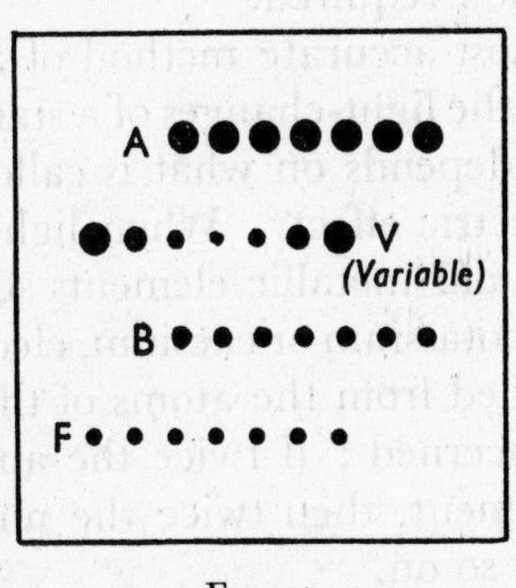

FIG. 27

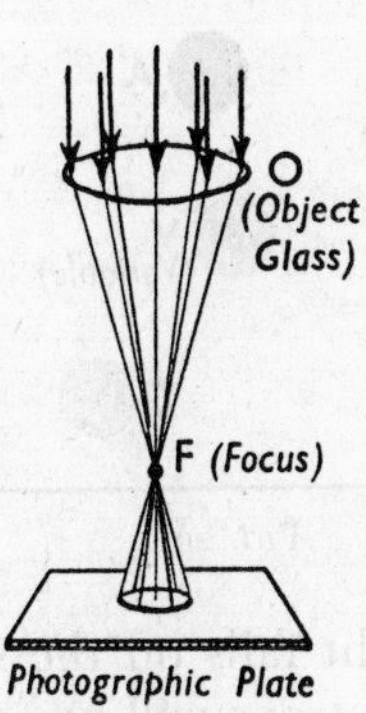

FIG. 28

A much more accurate method of obtaining the desired information by photography is by means of extra-focal images. In the method previously described the plate is "in focus"—that is to say the focus of the telescopic object glass lies on the sensitive surface of the photographic plate. In the extra-focal method the plate-holder is, by suitable mechanical means, moved some distance away from the focus as shown in exaggerated form in Fig. 28. The parallel beam of light falling on the object glass from the star is transformed into a converging conical beam with its apex at the focus and then diverging into a conical beam which, impinging on the plate, affects the sensitive actinic material over a circle of a particular diameter depending on the amount by which the telescope is out of focus;

this circle will be of the same size for all stars within the compass of the plate. The light which falls on the object glass is then, so to speak, distributed evenly over a given circular area of the plate.

If the star is bright, the photographic " blackening " of the plate will be intense ; if the star is faint, the corresponding circular area on the plate will only be slightly shaded. The appearance of the shaded areas is illustrated in Fig. 29. With a rather complicated instrument, the intensity of shading in the various extra-focal circles can be accurately measured and this can be correlated with the magnitude-differences of the reference stars ; the measurement of the intensity of the photographic blackening produced by the variable star can then be turned into the magnitude-information required.

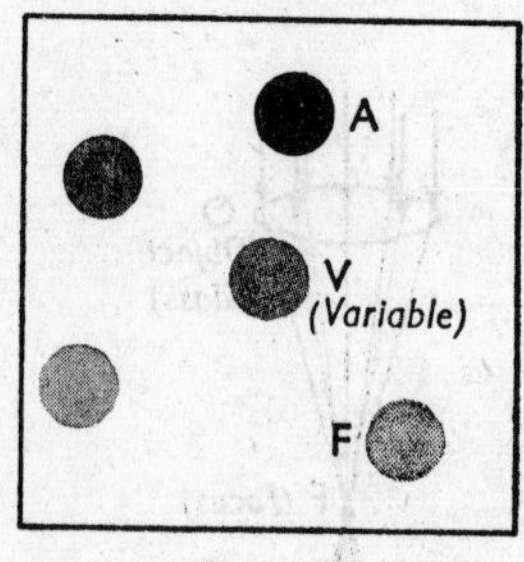

Fig. 29

The most accurate method of all for studying the light-changes of a star such as Algol depends on what is called the photo-electric effect. When light falls on particular metallic elements such as sodium, potassium or caesium, electrons are expelled from the atoms of the element concerned ; if twice the amount of light falls on the sensitive element, then twice the number of electrons will be expelled, and so on.

Evidently we have in the photo-electric effect an accurate means of comparing the relative brightness of two stars ; theoretically, all we have to do is to count the number of electrons emitted, say, by sodium in one minute by star A and then to count the number emitted by star B in the same interval. Just as a red and blue star of equal visual brightness—that is to say, of equal visual magnitudes—have different photographic effects, thus giving rise to different photographic magnitudes for the two stars, so the photo-electric scale of magnitude differs generally from both the visual and photographic scales and is dependent on the particular element used ; one element is most sensitive to blue light, another to red light and so on. But whatever element we use in the observations of, say, Algol we shall derive a light-curve of the general form shown in Fig. 26.

The principal part of the apparatus is the photo-electric cell which consists of a glass bulb the inside surface of which is coated with a thin film of the photoelectrically-sensitive element. The cell is mounted in or near the telescope focus and light from a star is admitted through a clear part of the glass at C (the window). Falling on the sensitive film, the light of the star expels electrons from the atoms of the element concerned ; the expulsion of electrons is immensely increased by applying as high a negative electric potential to the film as the latter can accommodate (Fig. 30).

The glass bulb is now to be pictured with its interior filled with flying electrons. A circular metal ring R at the end of a wire, securely insulated where it passes through the outlet O

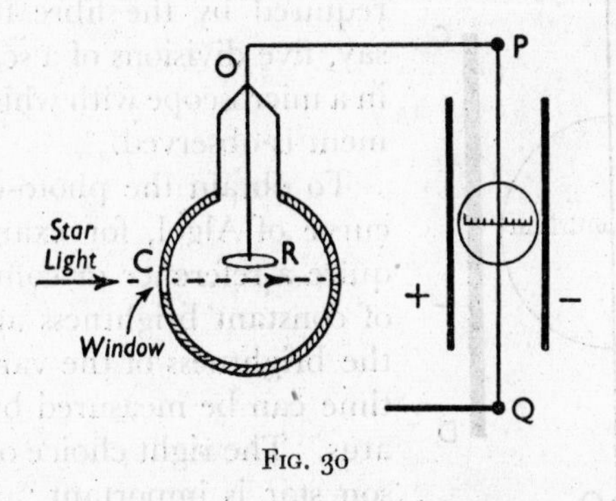

FIG. 30

from the cell, acts as a collector of the electrons—for this reason it is called the collecting-ring. The ring thus begins to be negatively charged as soon as light is admitted to the cell, and the greater the amount of light the greater will be the rate at which the ring is being charged. Instead of counting electrons —as we suggested at first—we measure the rate at which the collecting-ring is being charged.

As the forms of apparatus in present use are extraordinarily complicated we explain the principles of measuring the rate of charging of the ring in terms of the first instrument installed on the Sheepshanks Telescope at Cambridge Observatory. This instrument, called the string-electrometer, consisted of a silver-coated quartz fibre PQ (Fig. 30) kept taut by mechanical contrivances not shown in the figure. The upper extremity P is connected with the wire at one end of which is the collecting ring R; the other end at Q is insulated. Accordingly, the fibre, being silver-coated, becomes charged with negative electricity and the rate of charging of the fibre (or string) is the object of our observation. The fibre is mounted between two parallel metallic plates one of which is charged positively and the other negatively.

Suppose now that the fibre becomes negatively charged as a result of the photo-electric effect; it is attracted by the positively charged plate AB and repelled by the negatively charged plate CD (Fig. 31); the centre part of the fibre moves to the left and its rate of motion is measured by the time, given by a stop-watch, required by the fibre to pass over, say, five divisions of a scale mounted in a microscope with which the movement is observed.

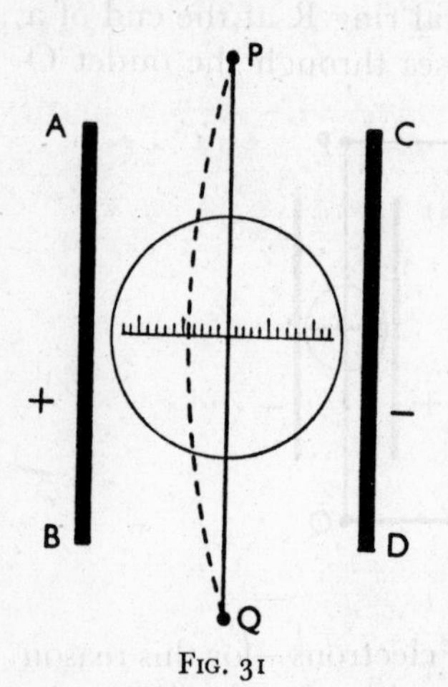

Fig. 31

To obtain the photo-electric light curve of Algol, for example, we require a reference or comparison star of constant brightness against which the brightness of the variable at any time can be measured by the apparatus. The right choice of a comparison star is important; it should be for obvious reasons of nearly the same magnitude as the variable when about half way between its maximum and minimum brightness. It should also be as near the variable in the sky as possible, for the light from each star, it has to be remembered, has to penetrate our atmosphere, being absorbed to an extent depending on the star's altitude. The effect of a small difference of altitude between the comparison star and the variable can be easily compensated; but when the difference in altitude is considerable, the compensation process is hedged with such uncertainty that the accuracy of the final result of an observation is seriously impaired. Also, for various reasons the comparison star and variable should be of as near the same colour as possible.

The nature of the observations may now be indicated briefly. The telescope is first turned on the comparison star and, with a stop-watch, a series of three timings of the motion of the electrometer fibre over a suitable number of divisions of the graduated scale is obtained with as little loss of time as possible ; it is to be understood that the G.M.T. corresponding to the beginning and end of a series is noted ; the G.M.T. for the middle of the series is then obtained. The telescope is then turned on the variable and a series of, say, five timings is obtained and the corresponding G.M.T., as described, is derived. The telescope is again turned with as little delay as possible on the comparison star and the observations repeated ; this second series is necessary since the transparency of the atmosphere is hardly likely

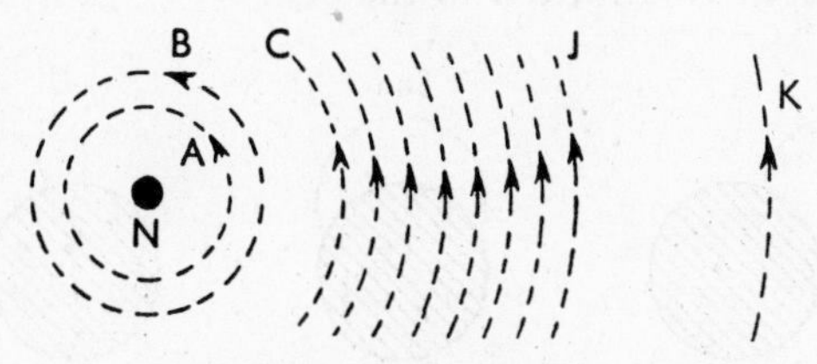

FIG. 32.—Sodium Atom

to remain absolutely constant and the most we can hope for is that the transparency will change at a uniform rate.

The average of the three or five timings is found for each series, and the average of the two results for the comparison star is then compared with the average of the single series observed for the variable star. In this way we get rid of the changeableness, however small it may be, of the atmosphere, for the effect of this procedure is to ensure that the observations of the comparison star and the variable refer substantially to the same instant of time. If the variable is changing in brightness then a continuous series of the observations described, alternating with respect to the comparison star and the variable, furnishes a succession of points on the light-curve.

Why is it that the ordinary light of a star has the capacity to expel electrons from the atoms of an element such as sodium? The answer is found in terms of the particular structure of the sodium atom. This atom (Fig. 32) consists of a nucleus N (built up of 11 protons and 12 neutrons) around which circulate first of all two electrons A and B near the nucleus, then a closely-related group of eight electrons, C to J, more remote from N, and finally a single electron K still farther away. This last electron is much more loosely held under the control of the nucleus than the others and the energy of ordinary light from a star is sufficient to expel the electron from the atom. In this state the atom is singly-ionised, but it does not remain so for more than the briefest moment as it captures an electron from the negative charge applied to the inner coating of the photo-electric cell. This newly acquired electron is immediately expelled by the light from the star ; and so the dual process of disruption and subsequent rehabilitation of the atom continues so long as light is admitted to the cell.

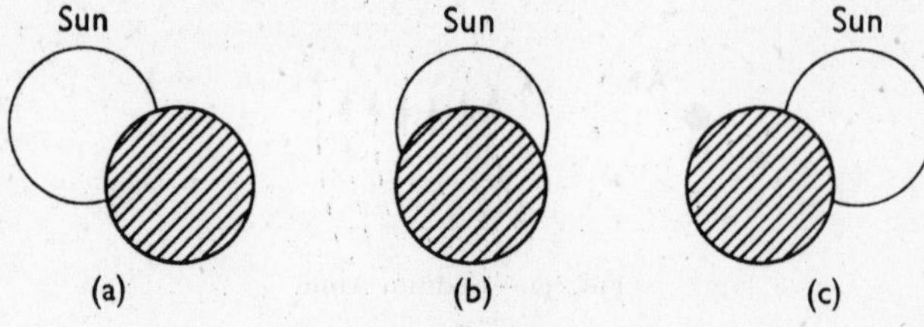

FIG. 33.—Partial Eclipse of Sun

We return now to Goodricke's explanation of the variability of Algol in terms of an eclipse of a bright star by a dark, or relatively dark, component. We are familiar with a comparatively frequent phenomenon, a partial eclipse of the Sun ; the occurrence of such an eclipse is due to the fact that the Moon interposes itself between us and the Sun, the three bodies Earth, Moon, and Sun being nearly in a straight line while the phenomenon lasts. The Moon is, of course, moving eastwards in the sky at a much greater angular rate than the Sun ; the eclipse begins just when the Moon is on the point of overtaking the Sun and ends when the Moon has just succeeded in getting clear of the Sun.

Fig. 33 (*a*) represents the situation shortly after the eclipse has started (the shaded circle represents the Moon's disc covering up a part of the Sun's disc) ; in this phase, the diminution of the Sun's light is, say, about one-fifth, this being the fraction of the Sun's disc covered by the Moon. Fig. 33 (*b*) represents the situation when the greatest fraction of the Sun's disc is covered up—if this fraction is, say, one-half, the Sun's light is dimmed by one-half. Fig. 33 (*c*) represents the circumstances when the eclipse is not far from being over.

It is to be noted that from the beginning of the eclipse to the instant represented by Fig. 33 (*b*), the blocking of sunlight by the Moon increases continuously although not at a constant rate, while after the instant represented by Fig. 33 (*b*) until the end of the eclipse the blocking of sunlight by the Moon diminishes continuously, again at a non-uniform rate. Fig. 33 (*b*) corresponds to *minimum* light. If we construct a light-curve based either on geometrical arguments (we can calculate, stage by stage, the fraction of the area of the Sun's disc not covered up by the Moon) or on observations of the intensity of sunlight throughout the eclipse, we shall obtain a light-curve with the general characteristics of the crude light-curve of Algol shown in Fig. 26 (page 89).

Conversely, if we are confronted with such a light-curve we can deduce certain geometrical relationships connected with the relative linear dimensions of the Sun and the Moon and their relative distances from the Earth.

The observed light-curve of Algol is a much more elaborate curve than the crude curve in Fig. 26. In Fig. 34 we show the light-curve based on photo-electric observations by H. E. Green and the author at Cambridge Observatory in the years 1930-31. The curve shows two distinct minima, the deep minimum at B (and at H), corresponding to the minimum of Fig. 26; almost exactly half-way between B and H there is a shallow minimum at E, called the *secondary minimum*. Now we have interpreted the occurrence of the principal minimum at B as the result of the partial eclipse of a luminous star by its dark, or relatively dark, companion; in the same way the secondary minimum at E is interpreted as the eclipse of the dark, or relatively dark, star by the more luminous body.

One noticeable feature of the light-curve is the small increase in brightness between C and D and a similar diminution of brightness between F and G—the range C to D, for example, corresponding to the interval between the ending of the partial eclipse of the bright star by the dark one and the beginning of the eclipse of the dark star by the bright one. Further, the secondary minimum at E occurs almost exactly between the successive principal minima at B and H from which one infers that, except in the event of certain exceptional circumstances, the orbit of the dark component around the bright one is a circle, or very approximately so. A third feature is that the brightness represented by the point E on the light-curve is perhaps just a little greater than the brightness represented by the point C (corresponding to the moment when the principal eclipse is just over).

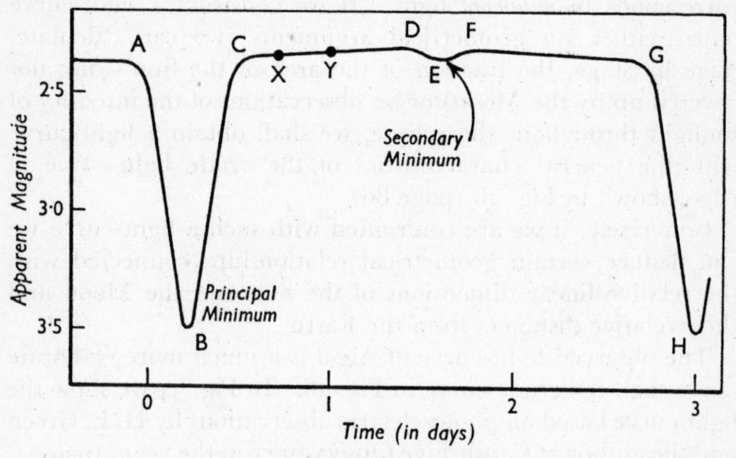

FIG. 34.—Light-Curve of Algol

To interpret these various features of the light-curve we have recourse to the geometrical combinations implied by the eclipse phenomena. Just as in the case of a solar eclipse the Earth, Moon and Sun must be nearly in the same straight line, so in the stellar case, at or near mid-eclipse, the Earth and the two components of Algol must be nearly in the same straight line. This implies that the line joining the Earth and Algol must lie almost in the plane of the orbit of the dark component around the bright star—in other words we are looking at the orbital plane almost edge on.

We represent the geometrical circumstances in Fig. 35 (*a*). S is the bright component round which revolves the dark star in a circular orbit. The dark star is shown at B_1 when it is between us and S and when the maximum area of the luminous disc of S is covered ; this corresponds to the principal minimum B of the light-curve (Fig. 34, page 100). Suppose X_1 is the position of the dark star a short time after the ending of the principal eclipse. If the dark star is entirely non-luminous, it has yet the capacity to reflect light just as the Moon reflects sunlight* ; a thin crescent of reflected light will be added to the brightness of S, very much like the lunar crescent near " new moon " ; this represents the circumstances at X on the light-curve. At Y_1 half the disc of the dark star is illuminated and the total illumination from the Algol-system has become greater ; this corresponds to Y on the light-curve (half-way between C and D). Just before the dark star, at D_1, passes behind

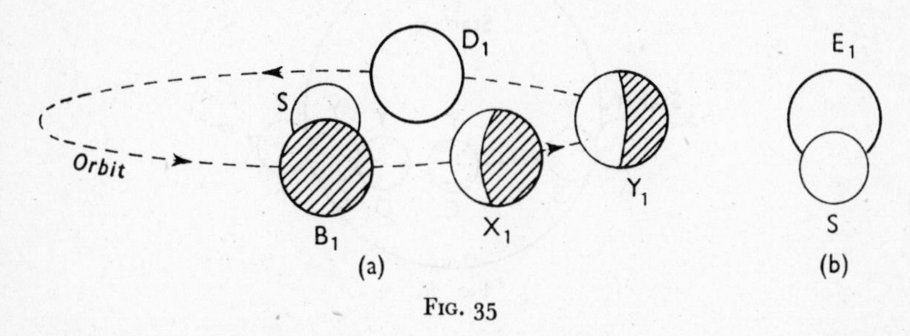

Fig. 35

S practically the whole disc turned towards us is illuminated just like " full moon " ; this corresponds to D on the light-curve, that is, when the Algol-system appears brightest.

When the dark star passes behind S, the phase of secondary minimum occurs ; if, as we assumed, the dark star is entirely non-luminous, the phase at minimum—Fig. 35 (*b*)—corresponds to the mid-point of the partial eclipse of the " full moon " and at mid-eclipse the total light of the Algol-system is the sum of the light of S (the bright star) and the light reflected from the uneclipsed part of the disc of the dark companion. Actually, the " dark star " is of very feeble luminosity inadequate, however, to make any substantial modification of the secondary minimum as previously described.

* The actual process of " reflection " is somewhat more complicated than suggested here.

In many cases of eclipsing binaries one of the eclipses is "total" and the other "annular"; in such instances the line between the Earth (or Sun) and the binary lies exactly, or almost exactly, in the plane of the orbit of one of the components around the other. Suppose that the components are X and Y and that X is larger than Y and, further, that the brightness of X per square yard of its surface is greater than the brightness of Y per square yard—this is tantamount to saying that the surface-temperature of X exceeds that of Y.

If, in Fig. 36, we consider the orbit of Y relative to X we have first of all an "annular" eclipse of X by Y in which Y appears projected against the disc of X, the annular phase being repre-

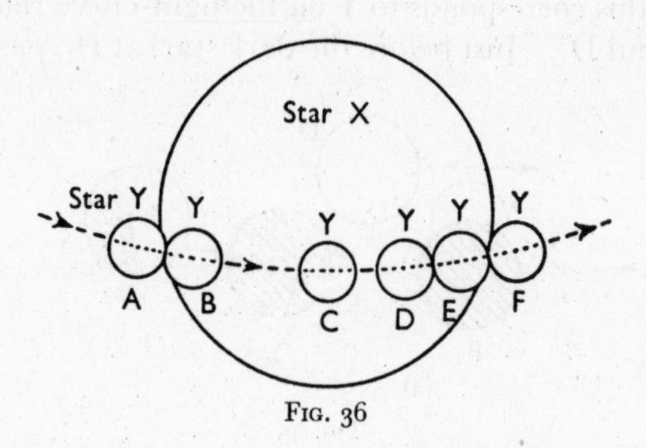

Fig. 36

sented by the series of positions from B to E. During this phase the proportion of the disc of X covered up by Y remains constant and, disregarding an effect to be referred to later, the light from the system remains constant. The partial phase of the eclipse begins when the star Y is in position A, and between A and B the light diminishes as Y covers up more and more of the disc of X. The end of the annular eclipse occurs at E and the succeeding partial eclipse ends when Y is just clear of the disc of X at F. The corresponding part of the light-curve (between A and F in Fig. 36) has the characteristics shown by the part $A_1B_1E_1F_1$ of Fig. 37.

The second eclipse in the binary we are considering occurs when Y is covered up by the large star X; since an area of the disc of X equal to the area of the disc of Y is much more luminous than Y—according to our assumption of the relative surface-temperatures—the diminution of light resulting from the total eclipse of Y must be less than the loss of light during the annular eclipse ; the circumstances of the eclipse of Y are represented by the part GHKL of the light-curve illustrated in Fig. 37.

There are several circumstances which imprint their individual features on a light-curve ; of these we mention one or two. In the instance we have just been considering (Fig. 36) we have assumed that the disc of the larger and more luminous component was of uniform brightness ; this is not exactly so. In the case of the Sun, for example, the intensity of light coming from the centre of the disc diminishes steadily towards the edge or " limb " of the Sun, a phenomenon known as " darkening towards the limb " and easily recognised on any photograph of

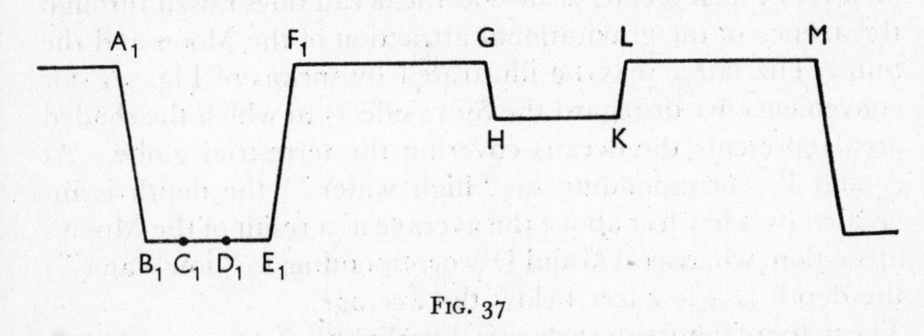

FIG. 37

the Sun. The cause of the phenomenon is simply due to the fact that the photospheric light coming from the centre of the disc has a much smaller thickness of solar atmosphere to traverse than light from the limb, the absorption of light increasing from centre to limb. A similar effect is observable on any cloudless day ; the Sun at noon is much brighter than at sunset, the diminution in brightness during the afternoon being due to the increasingly greater absorption resulting from the longer light-path in the terrestrial atmosphere as the Sun travels from its noon position in the sky towards the horizon.

The effect of " darkening towards the limb " on a minimum of the kind considered in Fig. 37 is shown in Fig. 38 in which the full-line curve represents the part of the light-curve under circumstances in which Fig. 37 was described, and the broken line the observed curve in which " darkening towards the limb" is conspicuous, the intensity at the centre of the disc being assumed to be the same in both cases.

Again we have implicitly suggested that the components of an eclipsing binary are *spherical* stars. In the case of eclipsing binaries in which the components are relatively far apart—as we shall see, these circumstances apply substantially to Algol—the stars depart comparatively little from the spherical form; but in very close binaries such as Beta Lyrae the gravitational attraction of one component on the other raises great gaseous tides on the stars, of much the same character—although on a very much greater scale—as the ocean tides raised through the agency of the gravitational attraction of the Moon and the Sun. The latter may be illustrated by means of Fig. 39 (for convenience we disregard the Sun's effect) in which the shaded area represents the oceans covering the terrestrial globe. At A and B (corresponding to "high water") the depth is increased by a few feet above the average as a result of the Moon's attraction, whereas at C and D (corresponding to "low water") the depth is a few feet below the average. The shape of the ocean-surface is thus slightly elongated, being approximately ellipsoidal. The gaseous material of a star responds far more effectively than water to gravitational attraction and, in the case of very close binaries, the stars are distorted into ellipsoids shaped much like rugby footballs.

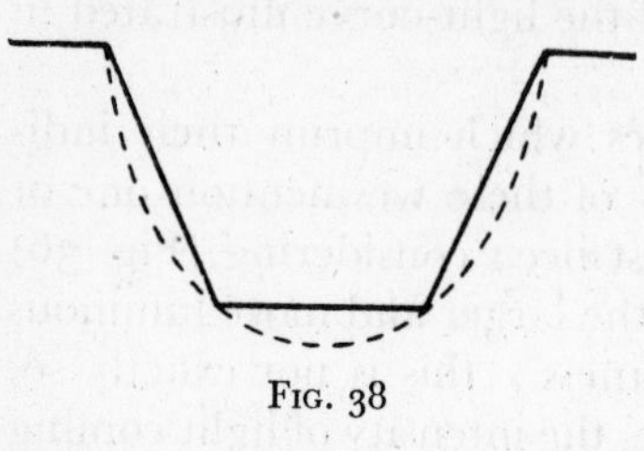

Fig. 38

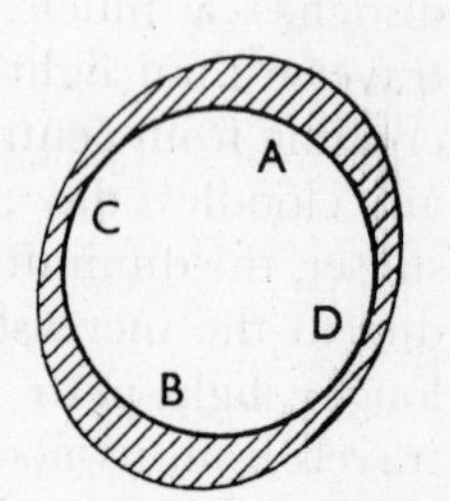

Fig. 39.—Lunar Tide

In addition to the effects of eclipses—and the effects are more complicated than in the case of spherical stars—we have the further complexity introduced by the shape of the disc presented to us by each star at any given moment, varying as it does from an elongated ellipse to approximately a circle. The interpretation of the light-curve of Beta Lyrae leads us to a picture of two ellipsoidal stars almost in contact, revolving about their common centre of mass with the greatest axis of one component pointing towards the centre of the other, as illustrated in Fig. 40.

It may be added that Goodricke discovered the variability of Beta Lyrae in 1784 suggesting as an explanation that the variable was actually a single bright star, rotating about an axis considerably inclined to the plane of the earth's orbit around the Sun, its surface being mottled with several permanent dark blotches resembling in this respect, except in the matter of scale and permanence, the solar disc with its short-lived sun-spots.

The verification by Vogel at Potsdam towards the end of the last century that Algol is in fact a binary system was one of the earlier achievements of astronomical spectroscopy. In the previous chapter we have briefly referred to the measurement of radial velocity and the application to the binary system of

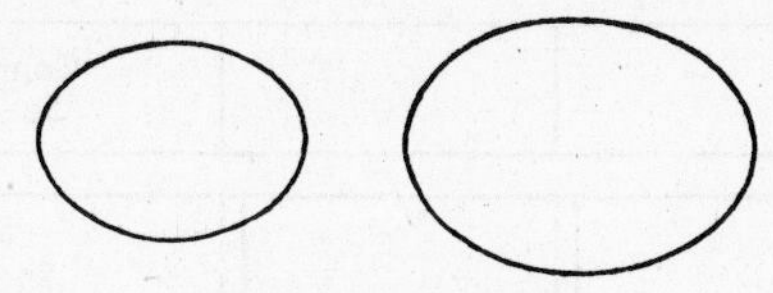

Fig. 40.—Beta Lyrae

Sirius. We here consider the principles involved in a rather more detailed way. We remind the reader that a particular element occurring in the reversing layer of the Sun or star reveals its presence by one or more dark, or absorption, lines with each of which is associated a definite wave-length accurately known from laboratory measurements.

We consider one particular qualification in connection with this apparently precise statement regarding the exact identity of laboratory wave-lengths with those derivable from the absorption lines of stellar spectra. It is a question of the effect of the motion of the star, towards us or away from us, in the line of sight. The explanation of this effect is usually prefaced by reference to an analogous phenomenon in connection with the changing pitch of a note, say, produced by an engine-whistle as a train rushes through a station. It is noticed that as soon as the train has passed us the pitch has dropped appreciably. The interpretation is that while the train is approaching us more sound-waves reach us per second than if the train were stationary, the train's speed being added, so to speak, to the normal speed of propagation of sound-waves emitted by a stationary source (or whistle), and that while the train is rushing away from us fewer sound-waves reach us per second than if the train were stationary.

In a similar way the " pitch " of the light-rays from a star is increased or decreased according as the star is approaching us or receding from us. As " pitch " varies inversely with wave-length we have the following qualitative conclusions : if a star is approaching us, all wave-lengths are diminished ; if the star is receding from us all wave-lengths are increased. We re-state this in terms of radial velocity and absorption lines, remembering that wave-lengths of the spectrum increase from

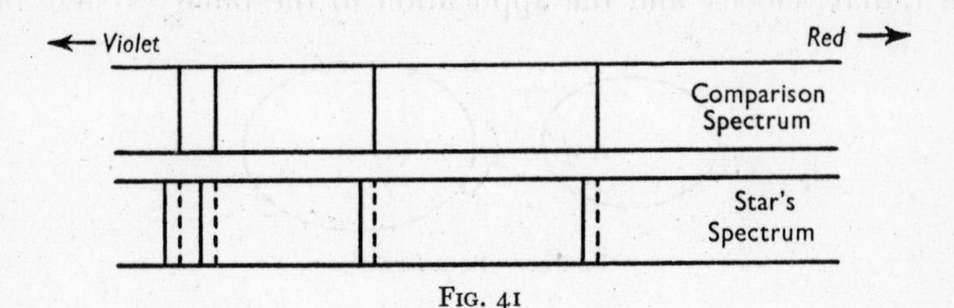

Fig. 41

the violet end towards the red end, as follows : If the radial velocity is one of approach, the absorption lines are displaced towards the violet end of the spectrum ; if the radial velocity is one of recession, the absorption lines are displaced towards the red end of the spectrum. This, together with a formula connecting the amount of the displacement of a particular line with radial velocity, is known as Doppler's principle.

We illustrate the case of a radial velocity of approach in Fig. 41. We have remarked on a previous occasion that the wave-lengths of absorption lines in a star's spectrum are measured with reference to standard lines produced, for example, by vaporised iron, the spectrograph attached to the telescope having the necessary facilities for producing the iron spectrum above the star's spectrum as shown in Fig. 41 and also below the star's spectrum (we omit this latter spectrum in the figure). We refer to the iron spectrum as the *comparison spectrum.* It should be added that the comparison spectrum is an emission spectrum consisting of bright lines ; in the figure these are shown, for convenience, in the same way as we represent the absorption lines of the star's spectrum (see also Plate IV (b), facing page 49).

For simplicity we shall suppose that the star's spectrum contains iron lines. If the star had a zero radial velocity the star's absorption lines would be in the positions given by the broken lines, each of which is a continuation of the corresponding iron line in the comparison spectrum. In the figure the star's iron lines are seen to be displaced towards the left—that is, towards the violet end of the spectrum—with respect to the corresponding lines of the comparison spectrum. The amount of the displacement (in angstrom units) can be measured and by the application of a simple formula the radial velocity of approach of a star can be readily found as so many miles per second.

In the same way the radial velocity of recession of a star can be obtained ; in this case the star's absorption lines are displaced to the right of the iron lines—that is, towards the red end of the spectrum.

We apply these principles to Algol. The spectrum of Algol is produced by the bright component ; the dark component, although slightly luminous, is ineffective in showing its presence in exposures of reasonable length. The binary system is, as a whole, moving in space relatively to us with constant velocity ; it follows, in terms of radial velocity, that the centre of mass of the two stars has a constant radial velocity ; this is found to be a velocity of recession of about 3½ miles per second.

Consider now the bright star which we shall assume, for simplicity, to be moving in a circular orbit—Fig. 42 (*a*)—around the centre of mass G, the line of sight OG being supposed for simplicity to be in the plane of the orbit. At A, the bright star is moving at right angles to the line of sight and thus its orbital motion at A makes no addition to the observed radial velocity of the system as a whole, namely, 3½ miles per second (recession). In this case a line X of the comparison spectrum —Fig. 42 (*b*)—will have its counterpart represented by the dotted line Y in the stellar spectrum such that the displacement between X and Y corresponds to the recessional velocity of $3\frac{1}{2}$ miles per second.

Consider now the bright star's position at B ; here the orbital velocity is directly away from us, so that, when the star is observed in this position (that is, at B), the line corresponding to X will appear at Z in the stellar spectrum, the displacement between X and Z corresponding to the sum of $3\frac{1}{2}$ miles per second and the star's orbital velocity at B, the latter being about 25 miles per second.

When the bright star is at C its orbital motion, being at right angles to the line of sight, makes no contribution to the observed radial velocity which will be $3\frac{1}{2}$ miles per second (re-

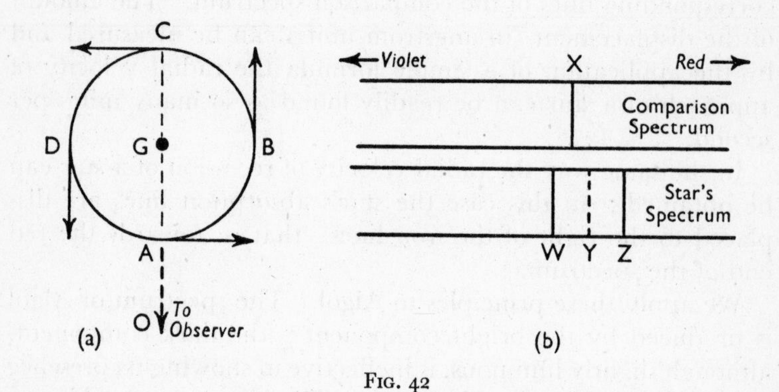

Fig. 42

cession) ; the corresponding line in the stellar spectrum will again be at Y. When the bright star is at D, its orbital motion will be directed towards us and the corresponding line—at W—will be displaced to the violet side of Y, the displacement Y to W being equal to the displacement Y to Z.

If the bright star is at any other point in its orbit the resulting absorption line will be somewhere between W and Z. If we then make a series of observations during the orbital period, an absorption line in the stellar spectrum will appear to oscillate between the positions W and Z and back again to W in a period equal to that of the light-curve. This is precisely what Vogel found in his observations and he concluded that the oscillatory phenomena were explicable in terms of the binary character of Algol.

The interpretation of the light-curve of an eclipsing variable is, in many cases, a rather tricky business owing to the many factors which contribute to its form and this is hardly the place to give a detailed account. One of the principal results is that we are enabled to make a model of the binary system, in which the radius of each star can be expressed in terms of the average separation of the two components, just as a knowledge of the orbital periods of the planets enables us to make a model of the solar system in terms of the astronomical unit ; also the relative brightness, per unit surface-area, of the two components can be obtained. Spectroscopic observations of the kind previously referred to furnish the means of expressing the average distance of the components in miles, from which the radii of the two stars can then be easily expressed also in miles. Also, in many cases, the mass of each component, the effect of " darkening towards the limb ", the ellipsoidal shape of the stars—and so on—can be deduced.

We conclude this chapter by giving some details of several eclipsing variables, beginning with Algol.

It should be stated that there is not complete unanimity in investigations of this famous star, for there are difficulties in the complete solution to which we have not referred ; further, the presence of a faint companion revolving around the close binary in a period of about 1¾ years adds complications and one effect is a slow change in the period of the light-curve.* But the following details, if not conveying quite general approval, will give the reader a picture of the eclipsing system. The two stars are separated by a distance of about 6½ million miles. The bright star, with a surface temperature of about 12,000°, has a radius of about 1⅓ million miles (about three times the solar radius) and a mass of about 4⅓ times the solar mass ; its average density is about one-fifth that of water. The dark and larger star, with a surface-temperature in the region of 3000°, has a radius of about 1½ million miles (about 3½ times the solar radius) and a mass rather less than that of the Sun ; its average density is about one-twentieth that of water. At the beginning of the chapter the name " Demon " may have suggested to the

* Since this was written the discovery of a still more distant component has been announced, revolving around the binary in a period of 188 years.

reader developments of a startling character ; instead—and perhaps disappointingly—Algol, as a binary, proves to be a perfectly harmless and unexceptional system.

The great majority of eclipsing binaries have periods of a few days only. The shortest period known is that of the variable known officially as UX Ursae Majoris, the period of which is just $4\frac{3}{4}$ hours. Such a short period implies that, on any reasonable hypothesis as to the total mass of the system, the two components must be much closer together than in the case of the components of Algol. If we assume that the mass of the system is twice that of the Sun, it is easily calculated that the separation of the components is about 800,000 miles. Suppose that each star resembles the Sun in size ; the two components would then be practically in contact—or even overlapping ! If the stars are almost in contact—as in the case of Beta Lyrae—each component would be distorted into ellipsoidal form through tidal action and the light-curve would not fail to reveal this fact.

On the contrary, the light-curve is definite in suggesting that the stars must be substantially spherical in form ; if this is so, tidal effects must be negligible and this inevitably leads to the conclusion that the components must be small stars with radii perhaps as large as one-third of the Sun's radius so that there is still a relatively large separation between the components. It is known that one of the stars has a surface-temperature of about 8000° and the inference is unescapable that this component must be of great density, although not perhaps quite rivalling the Companion of Sirius in this respect. It is believed from the available evidence that the surface temperature of the other component is in the region of 5000° and that, like its colleague, it is a small star of considerable density.

In great contrast with eclipsing binaries of the kind just described there are several well-known examples in which at least one component is a star of enormous dimensions. We shall refer to two of these : Zeta Aurigae and Epsilon Aurigae. The light-curve of Zeta Aurigae resembles, in general features, the light-curve drawn in Fig. 37. The period of light-changes is 972 days, or roughly 32 months ; the duration of the total eclipse of the smaller star by the larger is 39 days. The components consist of an immense and cool star, 16 times the mass of the Sun, and a hot and much smaller star, 9 times the mass of the Sun, the separation between the components being about 600 million miles. The larger star has a radius nearly 300 times that of the Sun while the radius of the smaller is about four times that of the Sun. In the post-war years the eclipses associated with this binary are eagerly looked forward to by astronomers in all parts of the world, for there are many points of interest in the spectroscopic observations still to be cleared up.

The second star referred to—Epsilon Aurigae—has the distinction of being the eclipsing binary with the longest period, 27 years 1 month ; the duration of a total eclipse is nearly a year. Also, with the possible exception of one of the components of the eclipsing binary VV Cephei, it shows us a star not surpassed in size by any other known star ; even the smaller component is matched by very few stars, its radius being one-tenth that of the larger star. The various investigations on Epsilon Aurigae are not quite concordant and the following details represent a rough average of the results derived from the observations. The brighter star is the smaller of the two ; the radius is about 200 times the Sun's radius ; its mass is about 28 times the solar mass ; its surface temperture is about 5000°. The fainter star is a giant of giants ; its radius is 2000 times the Sun's radius—nearly 900 million miles ; its surface-temperature is about 1200°, one of the lowest, if not the lowest, temperatures assigned to any luminary ; its mass is about 18 times the mass of the Sun. The average density of the smaller and more massive star is not far short of one-millionth that of water ; the average density of the gigantic component is one-thousandth that of the smaller star—a density of almost incredible tenuity.

In the previous chapter we showed where the densest matter in the universe was to be found ; in the case of the giant component of Epsilon Aurigae we pass to the other extreme. Nature certainly provided a surprise for astronomy in the white dwarfs ; the reader may quite well be of the opinion that she has provided a comparable surprise in the diffuse giant stars.

Chapter V

EPSILON AURIGAE, A GIANT STAR

So far there has been little difficulty in selecting the most prominent star in each of the three domains that have engaged our attention ; 61 Cygni must always be associated with the first successful accomplishment of measuring a star's distance and also with the detection of a body of planetary mass circulating round a star—just as the Earth or Jupiter circulates around the Sun ; it is certain that no astronomer would grudge the Companion of Sirius pride of place in the story of the detection of the unseen and in the discovery of matter of fantastic density ; nor is Algol likely to be displaced from its position as the most interesting, historically and intrinsically, of eclipsing stars.

But when we come to select for distinction one out of several giant stars each with its claim for consideration, it is scarcely likely that we should find unanimity in the ballot for the successful candidate. It is certain that Betelgeuse (Alpha Orionis)—the red giant in the shoulder of Orion—would have considerable support for, in addition to being one of the largest stars we know, it was one of the earliest (if not the earliest) to have its angular diameter measured by a new technique. Antares would also have its adherents because of its immensity, for its diameter is almost five hundred times the Sun's diameter. No doubt there would be one or two other candidates mainly on the score of size, such as Mira Ceti or Alpha Herculis or the larger component of Zeta Aurigae with which we were concerned in the last chapter (page 110) ; all of these stars are very large. The star which I propose to select as the most interesting giant star, although so little fame attaches to its name, is the large component of Epsilon Aurigae—partly because it is the largest star known (with a possible rival in VV Cephei) but principally because it seems nearer to the natal stage of a star's existence than any other we have so far encountered in astronomical investigations. It is this latter feature that we regard as of supreme interest in discussing the main theme of this chapter which we take to be the " evolution of the stars ". Our star then occupies probably a unique position amongst the immediate stellar population amid which the lot of the Sun and its planetary family is cast.

The position of Epsilon Aurigae is shown in the star-map in Fig. 43.

We recall that a giant star is in the first instance a star of great luminosity and, although there is no precise dividing-line

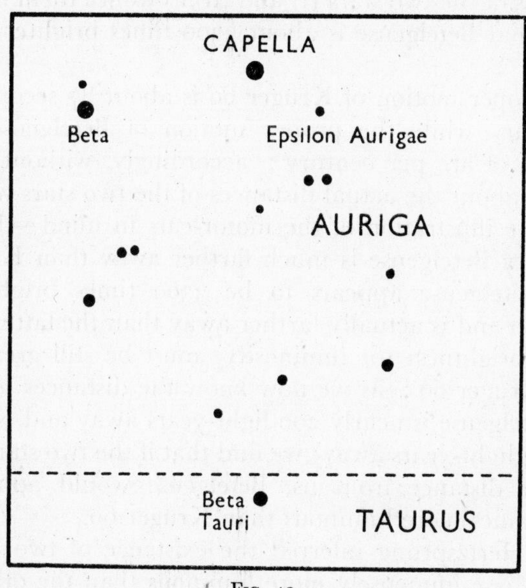

FIG. 43

between giants and dwarfs, it may be convenient to have in mind that giant stars are at least about fourteen or fifteen times more luminous than the Sun. The existence of two well-separated classes of red stars was first inferred by Hertzsprung about forty years ago. We have discussed the proper motions of the stars in some detail and we recall that a near star is likely to have a greater proper motion than a star much more remote —our example (page 41) of motor-cars travelling along two parallel roads illustrates the point. Hertzsprung noticed that several faint red stars had been found to have large proper motions and also to be amongst our nearest stellar neighbours, whilst several of the bright red stars had comparatively small proper motions and were much more distant than the former stars. We illustrate the point by referring to two red stars; (i) the brighter component of the binary Krüger 60, a star of the tenth magnitude (see page 39; the binary system is shown in Plate I (c), facing page 32), and (ii) Betelgeuse, a star of the first magnitude; for convenience we refer to the brighter component of the binary simply as Krüger 60. If we compare the brightness of the two stars (i) and (ii) as we see them in the sky, we find that Betelgeuse is about 3300 times brighter than the former.

The proper motion of Krüger 60 is about 87 seconds of arc per century while the proper motion of Betelgeuse is only 3 seconds of arc per century; accordingly, without knowing anything about the actual distances of the two stars we infer—having the illustration of the motor-cars in mind—that in all probability Betelgeuse is much farther away than Krüger 60. But if Betelgeuse appears to be 3300 times brighter than Krüger 60 and is actually farther away than the latter, then its intrinsic brightness (or luminosity) must be still greater than that of Krüger 60; as we now know the distances of the two stars (Betelgeuse is nearly 200 light-years away and Krüger 60 is only 13 light-years away) we find that if the two stars were at the same distance from us, Betelgeuse would appear over 800,000 times more luminous than Krüger 60.

Thus, Hertzsprung inferred the existence of two classes of red stars, one immensely more luminous than the other; the former he designated *giants* and the latter *dwarfs*. With our more accurate and complete information, including that of surface-temperature, gathered in later years, we can calculate the radii of the two stars; Betelgeuse is a giant in dimensions having a radius of 94 million miles (about 290 times the radius of the Sun) while Krüger 60 is a dwarf star with a radius of 147,000 miles, about one-third that of the Sun.*

Can the existence of immense stars such as Betelgeuse be

* The radius of the Sun, it will be recalled, is 432,000 miles; it may be added that the radius of Betelgeuse fluctuates somewhat, but that need not concern us as regards the average size of its radius.

checked by observation or reasoning of a wholly different character, for perhaps there might be some flaw in the calculations just alluded to? We have seen in the previous chapter that we can derive the sizes of the components of many eclipsing binaries and in several instances, one or other of the components is inferred to be of immense dimensions; the larger component of Zeta Aurigae with a radius of about 130 million miles and the larger component of Epsilon Aurigae with a radius of nearly 900 million miles are cases in point.

Another method of deducing the sizes of the giant stars such as Betelgeuse was applied successfully at Mt. Wilson Observatory. The angular diameter of the Sun as we see it in the sky is a little over half a degree—in Fig. 44 it is the angle AEB subtended by the Sun's diameter AB, of 864,000 miles, at the Earth E, 93 million miles away. If we imagine the Sun to be

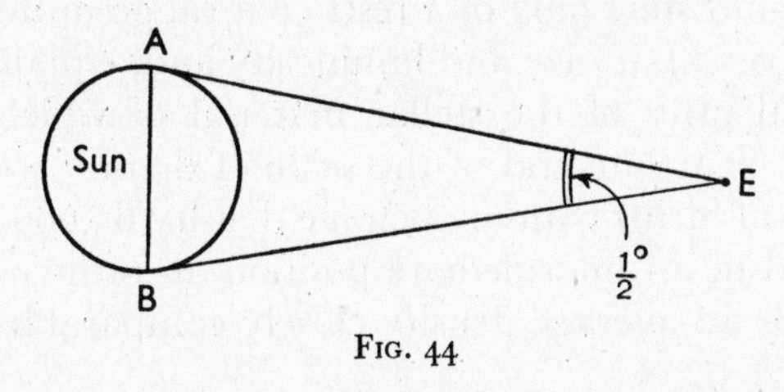

FIG. 44

moved farther and farther away from the Earth the angular diameter will shrink and if the Sun is as far away as the nearest star its angular diameter would be about seven thousandths of a second of arc and if it were as far away as Betelgeuse the angular diameter would be about one-seventh of a thousandth part of a second of arc; in either case, its disc would shrink away to a mere point of light.

But if we assume that Betelgeuse has the immense size which we inferred from calculations would the angular diameter of its disc be large enough to be measured? It is certain that we could not *see* the disc of the star in the ordinary way even in the biggest telescope, but by means of certain optical principles incorporated in an instrument called the "interferometer" the angular diameter of Betelgeuse yielded to measurement and was found to be about one-twentieth of a second of arc; from the known distance of Betelgeuse we can then find the dimensions of the star and the result was found to be in almost exact agreement with that obtained by calculations. The successful application of this new technique to the measurement of the sizes of Betelgeuse and several other stars was one of the very great astronomical achievements of the present century and it assured astronomers that there was no real flaw in the method of *calculating* the sizes of the stars when their distances and surface-temperatures were known.

The study of binary stars, such as Sirius, enables us as we have seen to derive the masses of the stars in terms of the Sun's mass as unit and, as we have mentioned, the great majority of the stars have masses between a fifth of the Sun's mass and five times the Sun's mass. There are, of course, stars with masses somewhat outside the limits just mentioned. We shall see later that there is something like a conspiracy on the part of Nature to build stars only of a restricted range in mass despite their vast diversity in size and luminosity and, equally notably, in average density of the stellar material of which they are composed. Near one end of the scale of density we have the Companion of Sirius with an average density 65,000 times that of water and in an intermediate position an ordinary star like the Sun with an average density closely comparable with that of water.

If the giant stars have masses, say a score of times that of the Sun, then consideration of their enormous bulk leads to the conclusion that the average density of such stars is almost unbelievably minute. For example, it turns out that the matter of which Betelgeuse is composed is about 1500 times more rarefied than air ; Antares is about twice more rarefied than Betelgeuse and our selected star, the larger component of Epsilon Aurigae, is hundreds of times more rarefied still. With the most efficient vacuum-pump at our disposal, it would be found impossible to exhaust the air from a flask to a less density than is found in these giant stars.

The contrast between the extreme states of matter existing in the stars—the fantastically immense density of the Companion of Sirius on the one hand and the equally fantastically low density of the giants we have mentioned on the other—is indeed remarkable. Can this diversity throw any light on the problems as to how the stars come into being, how (if at all) they change their physical characteristics during the long aeons of cosmogonic time? Can we, in fact, assert that there is a process of stellar evolution? The answers to such questions require the consideration of further well-established observational data and take us into regions where exploration is only possible through the application of physical principles.

When the spectra of a few stars had been obtained in the early days of astronomical spectroscopy, it was at once noticed that there were significant dissimilarities, first as regards the number of absorption lines and of the elements associated with them and, second, as regards the relative intensities in the different parts of the continuous (or rainbow) spectrum. Some had a wealth of absorption lines denoting the presence of various elements such as hydrogen, calcium, iron, aluminium and so on, in the atmospheres of the stars, while others showed only a few lines, usually of hydrogen and helium. Some showed the absorption bands characteristic of such compounds as the oxides of titanium and zirconium; others, only a few, showed bright emission lines. The first general object of spectroscopists was to attempt a classification of spectra according to such general principles as appeared to be of influence in producing the diversity of spectra observed.

The classification of spectra now adopted is one based principally on the origin and characteristics of the absorption lines which give a clue to the temperatures and densities of the stellar atmospheres (or outer layers). We have had occasion to refer to surface-temperature and it is convenient here to indicate in tabular form the relation between temperature and the various spectral classes or types. The principal of these are designated in sequence by the letters

O, B, A, F, G, K, M

the dislocation in alphabetical order and the omission of various letters testifying to the changing ideas as regards the progression from one type to another.

It should be mentioned, too, that each class is subdivided on a decimal basis; for example, G_5 means a spectrum midway between the beginning of the G class (denoted by G_0) and the beginning of the K class (denoted by K0). Further, there are slight variations between the giants and the dwarfs of the same spectral class ; the letters g and d are used to distinguish these ; it is to be noted that this subdivision begins at G0. The relation between surface-temperature and spectral class is shown in the folowing table (compiled from various sources) :

Table : Temperatures according to spectral class

Spectral Class	*Temp.*	*Spectral Class*	*Temp.*	*Spectral Class*	*Temp.*
O	40,000°	g G0	5600°	d G0	6000°
B0	23,000°	g G5	4700°	d G5	5500°
B5	15,000°	g K0	4200°	d K0	5100°
A0	11,000°	g K5	3400°	d K5	4400°
A5	8500°	g M0	3100°	d M0	3400°
F0	7400°	g Me *	2300°		
F5	6500°		1650°		

There is also, in general, a correlation between spectrum and colour ; the O and B stars are blue, the A and F are white, G stars are yellow, K are orange and M are red—the variation in colour is easily seen in the telescope although to the unaided eye the diversity in colour is not so apparent.

We add a few remarks of a general nature on the preceding table. It is convenient to start with the cooler stars of type M in which the surface-temperature is round about 3000° ; this temperature is sufficiently high to disrupt the vast majority of compounds such as common salt, water, carbon-dioxide and so on—if such ever existed as compounds in the Sun or stars—into their constituent elements ; for example, common salt, which is the chloride of sodium, would be broken up easily at the temperature prevailing, into sodium atoms and chlorine atoms ; the presence of the former in the stellar atmosphere is disclosed by a pair of close absorption lines in the yellow part of the spectrum, known as the D lines of sodium. But the temperature in the stellar atmosphere of M type stars is not sufficiently high to break up the molecules of such refractory compounds as titanium oxide the presence of which is disclosed by a series

* Me denotes an M-type spectrum with bright or emission lines and as these stars are variable in temperature the maximum and minimum temperatures are shown.

of absorption bands forming a prominent feature of the spectra of stars of this class.

The molecular bands persist in Class K in which the lines due to calcium become prominent. In class G, (to which the Sun belongs—it is a G0 star) the absorption lines of hydrogen and of many metals such as sodium, iron, aluminium and so on are strongly in evidence. In class F the metallic lines begin to fade out and in class A hydrogen attains its greatest prominence in any of the types. In B and O types the absorption lines are mainly those of hydrogen and helium.

In Chapter III (page 81) we have described the process of ionisation—the disruption of atoms under the conditions prevailing in the stars. Consider the atmosphere of a star such as the Sun ; heat-energy is flowing from the centre of the Sun outwards through the outer layers into space. This heat-energy may be sufficiently powerful to remove the outermost electron of an atom such as calcium and the atom, so bereft, is referred to as the singly-ionised atom of calcium which has its own distinctive spectrum. The singly-ionised calcium atom can thus produce characteristic absorption lines ; in the solar spectrum (and in many stellar spectra) we have two prominent lines—called the H and K lines—arising from the presence of singly-ionised calcium. It may be added, parenthetically, that these two lines play a most important part in our exploration of space.

It is not to be supposed that the calcium atoms need remain ionised perpetually ; the solar atmosphere has now a swarm of electrons rushing about and, if the circumstances of temperature and density are favourable, an ionised atom may capture a wandering electron and so may have its complete array of planetary electrons restored. But very soon a quantum of radiation of the right energy will fall upon the reconstituted atom and ionise it once more ; at a given instant there is then a balance in the relative numbers of ionised and of un-ionised atoms.

In a star hotter than the Sun the proportion of ionised atoms to un-ionised will be greater than for the Sun and for a still hotter star all the calcium atoms will be ionised, some singly and some doubly. Without going into further details, it can be seen that an understanding of ionisation processes, built up on laboratory experiments and theoretical considerations, is a great aid to the thorough interpretation of stellar spectra in terms of the physical conditions prevailing in stellar atmospheres ; it is evident, however, that stellar spectra provide a most complicated and difficult problem the solution of which demands a highly skilled knowledge of atomic physics in all its many ramifications ; part of the fruits of this study is shown in the table on page 118.

So far in this sketch of stellar classification we have confined ourselves to a discussion of absorption lines. The continuous spectrum—or rather the part of it which is not blotted out by absorption lines and bands—can also make its contribution. If we ask why a particular star is red in colour the continuous spectrum can provide the answer, for the greatest intensity of light is found in the red part and minimum intensity in the blue part, with the result that the predominant colour is red. Similarly, the continuous spectrum of the O and B stars shows the greatest intensity in the blue part of the visible spectrum and that is why they appear to us to be blue. Physical laws tell us that the progression of maximum intensity from red to blue is a progression of increasing temperature ; the M type stars—that is, the red stars—have a lower surface temperature than the K type or orange stars and so on through the special classes to the O type stars which are the hottest of all ; the table on page 118 shows this progression of temperature with spectral class in detail.

In the early years of the present century the great activity in the measurement of stellar distances led to a considerable amount of information relating to the intrinsic luminosities of the stars or, expressed in a more convenient form, the absolute magnitudes of the stars. Luminosity—or absolute magnitude —is thus an index of one physical characteristic of a star, namely, the rate of radiation of heat and light energy from a star ; as we have seen the luminosity of a star depends on the extent of its surface-area—that is to say its size—and on the surface-temperature. We have just referred to the relation between surface-temperature and spectral class and we now enquire what is the relation, if any, between a star's luminosity (or absolute magnitude) and spectral class.

Just before the beginning of the first world war Professor Hertzsprung and Professor H. N. Russell independently exhibited the relationship in the form of a diagram. To illustrate the main features we refer to Fig. 45 which is based, as regards its chief characteristics, on Russell's original diagram. In addition to measuring the distances of about 50 stars himself, Russell collected all the other relevant information available at the time; he had then for each of several hundreds of stars (i) the absolute magnitude and (ii) the spectral type. Marking off the absolute magnitude vertically and the spectral type

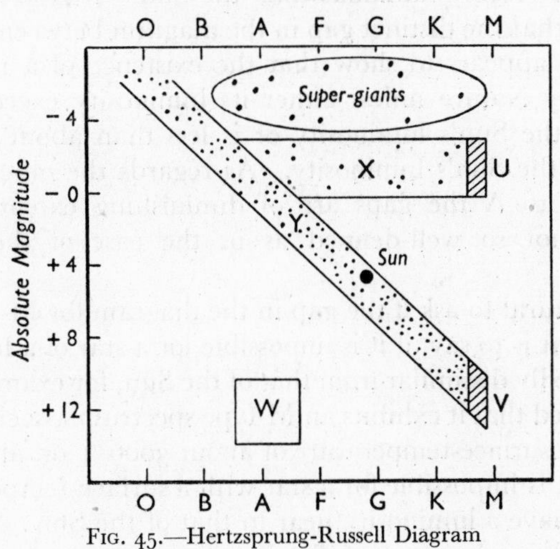

FIG. 45.—Hertzsprung-Russell Diagram

horizontally, he could then represent by a dot on the diagram the position of a star of known absolute magnitude and spectral type; for example, the Sun, of absolute magnitude 4·8 and spectral type G0, is specially represented in Fig. 45. Russell found a significant distribution of the dots (a number of which are shown in the figure); with a few exceptions, they lay either on the horizontal area marked X or the transverse area marked Y.

Consider first the stars of spectral type M. The diagram seemed to show that they could be divided into two groups, lying in parts of the diagram, one indicated by U and the other by V. The least luminous of the group in U is of absolute magnitude about +2; a star with this absolute magnitude is about 14 times more luminous than the Sun. The first group, U, then consists of stars each of which is at least 14 times more luminous than the Sun. The most luminous star in the group V has an absolute magnitude of about +8; it is thus only about one-eighteenth as luminous as the Sun; consequently the second group consists of stars with feeble luminosity as compared with the Sun. The diagram shows then the division of the M-type stars into two categories of giants and dwarfs, the former very much more luminous than the Sun and the latter much more feebly luminous than the Sun. It is to be further observed that the distinct gap in the diagram between the areas U and V appears to show that the existence of a red star is banned by Nature unless either its luminosity exceeds about 14 times the Sun's luminosity or is less than about one-eighteenth of the Sun's luminosity. As regards the other spectral classes K to A the gaps are of diminishing extent and are actually not so well-defined as in the case of the M-type stars.

It is natural to ask if the gap in the diagram for M-type stars is real, that is to say, if it is impossible for a star of a luminosity not markedly dissimilar from that of the Sun, for example, to be so fashioned that it exhibits an M-type spectrum associated with which is a surface-temperature of about 3000°; or, alternately, to ask if it is impossible for a star with a surface-temperature of 3000° to have a luminosity near to that of the Sun. In earlier work on the measurement of stellar distances it was natural for astronomers to concentrate their attention—so far as the red stars were concerned—first, on the bright red stars, for apparent brightness suggested the possibility that such stars were comparatively near and therefore likely to furnish relatively accurately results, or second, on the faint red stars of large proper motion for, as we have seen, large proper motion is an almost certain index of nearness to us, so that once more the astronomer would be reasonably assured of a definite result of his labours. In the first category he was, as we now know, undoubtedly selecting stars of high luminosity for his measurements and, in the second, stars of feeble luminosity. The gap in the Hertzsprung-Russell diagram might then be a consequence of the way in which stars were selected for the arduous procedure of distance-measurement. In the intervening years the gap remained stubbornly unclosed, although the possibility that selection still plays a part is constantly being borne in mind.

The stars in the transverse area, Y, of the Hertzsprung-Russell diagram are called stars of the *main sequence*—they start with the giants of class O and B and finish up with the faint red dwarfs of type M. It would seem that by far the greatest proportion of the stars belong to the main sequence. Some years ago Hertzsprung, using very accurate observational material relating to the Pleiades, demonstrated the characteristics of the main sequence in a very interesting way. The Pleiades are a compact group of stars in the sky—on a clear night a normal eye should be able to detect at least seven of the group ; a telescope will reveal several hundreds more (see

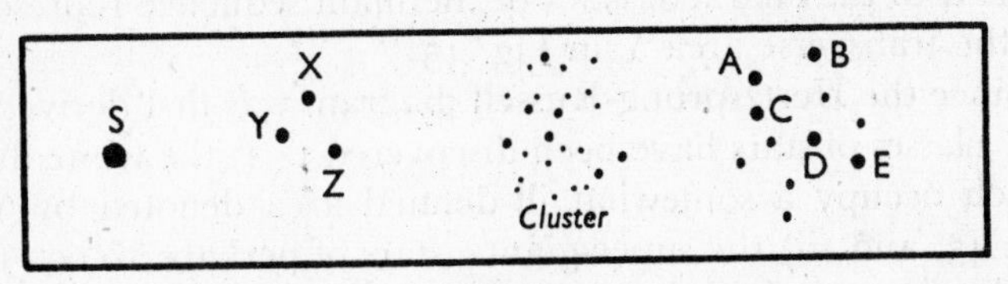

FIG. 46

Plate V (a), facing page 128). The remarkable thing about the Pleiades is that the stars form a compact group or cluster *in space*, all the members of which are travelling in parallel directions with the same speed, just like the individuals in a massed battalion of the Guards moving across the parade ground. The common motion in a definite direction in space is shown up by the fact that all the stars of the cluster have the same proper motion both as regards amount and as regards direction. In this way the cluster stars can be distinguished from ordinary stars seen in the direction of the Pleiades but at distances considerably different from that of the cluster itself ; in Fig. 46, S represents the Sun from the neighbourhood of which we make our observations ; X, Y and Z are stars in the direction of the cluster but on the nearer side ; A, B, C . . . are stars farther off than the cluster. All of these stars are of course likely to be seen in the telescope but, as has been said, they can be ruled out so far as membership of the cluster is concerned because of the dissimilarity of their proper motions from those of the cluster stars.

We simplify our explanation by supposing that we can measure accurately the distance of any cluster star—this is then effectively the distance of every member, for the dimensions of the cluster are small compared with its distance from us. We can now easily find the absolute magnitude of every star in the cluster, since the measurement of apparent magnitude presents little difficulty. Hertzsprung succeeded further in deriving what is the equivalent of the spectral type of each star. He had now—we suppose—all the information for plotting absolute magnitude against spectral type as in the Hertzsprung-Russell diagram ; the result of this investigation showed that all the stars of the Pleiades—from B type to M type—conformed to the characteristics of the main sequence represented by the transverse area Y in Fig. 45.

Since the Hertzsprung-Russell diagram was first derived two new classes of stars have been discovered : (i) the white dwarfs which occupy a somewhat ill-defined area denoted by W in Fig. 45, and (ii) the super-giants, stars of perhaps 10,000 times the luminosity of the Sun and of various spectral types, occupying an area shown at the top of Fig. 45.

When the Hertzsprung-Russell diagram was first established, the question of the relationship between the evolution of the stars and the statistical results disclosed in the diagram became one of considerable interest. We must make it clear at the outset that stars evolve, in some respects, just like the organisms with which we are familiar. The stars pour out vast quantities of heat and light energy ; evidently they are losing something and are changing in the process. We are familiar with various forms of energy ; the cannon-ball, travelling with a speed of several hundred feet per second, has energy of motion by virtue of which it can do work, say, in breaching a fortification ; heat and light energy and the energy of radio waves are all forms of electromagnetic energy ; a large boulder poised precariously high up on the side of a hill is said to have potential energy which is the capacity of doing work,—for example, in knocking down a tree at the bottom of the hill, if it is displaced from its state of rest; in this case potential energy is converted into energy of motion.

In 1906 Einstein established the equivalence of mass and energy, and so mass has to be added to the other forms of energy already noted. The energy locked up in, say, the mass of a brick is stupendous but, fortunately or unfortunately, this energy cannot be tapped to any significant extent by any process so far known. We shall see, however, that in the stars a comparatively minute proportion of the mass-energy of stellar matter is being constantly drawn upon to maintain the star as a luminous body.

If, then, a star is radiating heat and light energy into space by the apparently simple process of shining, it follows from Einstein's principle that this dissipation of energy is equivalent to loss of mass; accordingly, the star "shines away" part of its mass. In the sense, then, that the mass of a star is diminishing,—and, as we shall see, changing in its physical and chemical attributes—we can use the term "evolution" in application to the luminous orbs of the sky. In this case evolution is a slow process, slow compared with the almost explosive character of the change of some stars—the so-called "new stars"—from a lowly and undistinguished state to a condition of brief splendour, followed by a gradual decline to obscurity and to a condition probably little different from that preceding the outburst.

If, then, we agree that a normal star evolves in the sense indicated—we leave "new" stars out of the present discussion—can we say or guess how such a star started on its evolutionary career? It is generally agreed that a star begins life as an immense, diffuse and cool globe of atoms, molecules and small particles, drawn together by gravitational attraction; the nearest to this state that we can observe in the sky is precisely the giant component of our selected star Epsilon Aurigae. To simplify matters we shall suppose that this vast globe is far removed from its brighter companion in the binary system and so can be regarded as a single star remote from all other stellar influences.

Russell's original theory of stellar evolution, based on the diagram on Fig. 45, is briefly as follows. As the result of gravitational attraction the globe begins to shrink in size—the matter of the outermost layer falls a little towards the centre and so, similarly, do the other layers with the result that there is a decrease in potential energy. The pressure and density at any particular level increases a little and, further, since energy is indestructible, the potential energy lost by contraction is converted into heat energy. The process of contraction is thus accompanied by increase of temperature throughout the globe and after this process has continued for some considerable time the globe becomes sufficiently hot as to be faintly luminous; the globe accordingly has become a star. As contraction proceeds further the star becomes hotter and denser; when the surface-temperature rises to about 3000° we have the characteristic signs of an M-type star.

As contraction continues the compression and temperature of the star increase and the star passes through successively the phases associated with the conditions in the stars of types K, G, F, A and B. So far, the well-known physical laws of gases enable us to keep track of the changes described. But as late as 1924 it was considered that after the star had reached type B the laws of gases could no longer apply, for the average density of such stars was approaching that of water, and it was then surmised that further contraction would be so slow that the resulting increase of temperature would be insufficient to counterbalance the loss of heat by the ordinary process of radiation; the star must then gradually cool and if there were sufficient time it could then pass through the spectral classes in the reverse order—namely B, A, F, G, K and M—finishing up as a faintly luminous dwarf of type M.

This in brief is the celebrated theory of stellar evolution propounded by Russell in the middle of the second decade of the present century. It may be asked if the theory had any observational support. In the first place it could not be denied that in the heavens there were stars of all spectral classes and, if evolution be granted, these classes could quite well represent the various stages of the process envisaged. Secondly, there was plenty of evidence to show that stellar densities increased in a progressive way from the exiguous density of the cool giant M stars backward through the spectral series to the hot stars of type B and then in the reverse order to the cool dwarfs of type M in which the average density of the stellar material was perhaps a hundred times the density of water.

On this view of evolution the giant M stars must be regarded as " young ", having barely started on their stellar life, and the dwarf M stars as " old ", perhaps not far away in time from the close of their careers as luminous bodies. The stellar population was, in fact, very much like the human population representing every age from the babe in arms to the octogenarian, our star Epsilon Aurigae resembling a babe just newly born. Presumably, then, according to this theory the birth of stars is proceeding continuously in the depths of space where matter is first gathered together by gravitation into vast globes of atoms while, at the same time, the barely luminous dwarf stars are well on their way to extinction.

There is a further feature of the supposed progression from M type giants to M type dwarfs, not sufficiently realised at first owing to the scantiness of observational data available at the time. This was the fact that along the supposed evolutionary route there was a diminution of mass from the giant red stars of about twenty solar masses to the B stars of five to ten solar masses, thence to stars of solar mass, and at the end the red dwarfs with masses as low as one-seventh of the Sun's mass. We have seen that a star's mass diminishes through the simple process of shining ; to take the Sun as an example we know the present rate at which it is radiating heat and light energy, and by Einstein's principle we can transform this into the rate at which the solar mass is diminishing. The result is that the Sun is shedding in one minute a mass of about 240 million tons, which at one time was roughly the total annual production of coal in Great Britain. This may seem a prodigious rate of squandering of substance, but the Sun's mass is so enormous—it is

2,000 million million million million tons—

that if this rate had been kept up ever since the time the Sun's mass was double its present mass the interval required would be about 16 million million years and still larger if the Sun started as a globe of twenty times its present mass.

The time required for evolution in the sense described is evidently almost immeasurably long and the question naturally arises as to the legitimacy of assigning such enormous ages to the stars of dwarf characteristics. A further question concerns the adequacy (or otherwise) of the contraction process to provide the star with the requisite energy to maintain its existence as a luminous globe. We shall first consider the second question and see if it is consistent with the vast ages which appear to result from Russell's theory of evolution.

It was Helmholtz and, particularly, Lord Kelvin who first gave precision to the solution of the problem of a diffuse globe contracting through gravitational attraction. The problem stated more precisely is : assuming that the Sun was originally an immense diffuse globe, how long would it take to shrink to its present size so that the rate of diminution of potential energy is equivalent to the rate at which heat and light energy is at present radiated from the solar surface ? The answer depends on the present distribution of density in the Sun but, however we assess this, the age of the Sun—reckoning from the time at which it started as a diffuse globe—cannot be more than about 50 million years. A century ago this result, bearing the immense authority of Kelvin, caused dismay amongst geologists and biologists who, arguing from the reasonable assumption that the Sun must be at least as old as the Earth, saw that the processes of Nature required a vastly greater age for the Earth than 50 million years. For example, the immense thicknesses of the sedimentary rocks, slowly formed by the deposition of solid material carried by the rivers and glaciers to the ocean beds, could not be accounted for unless the process of formation of these rocks were spread over very much longer periods of time than Kelvin's calculations indicated ; fossil-remains presented a similar difficulty. The conflict between the findings of physics, as represented by Kelvin's calculations on the one hand, and the much longer time-requirements of geology and biology on the other was one of the outstanding episodes of nineteenth century science and was only settled in favour of the latter at the close of the century when the phenomenon of radioactivity was discovered and applied to the estimation of the ages of the rocks.

V(a). Pleiades cluster, with meteor trail
(W. J. S. Lockyer)

(b). Globular cluster in Hercules
(Mt. Wilson Observatory)

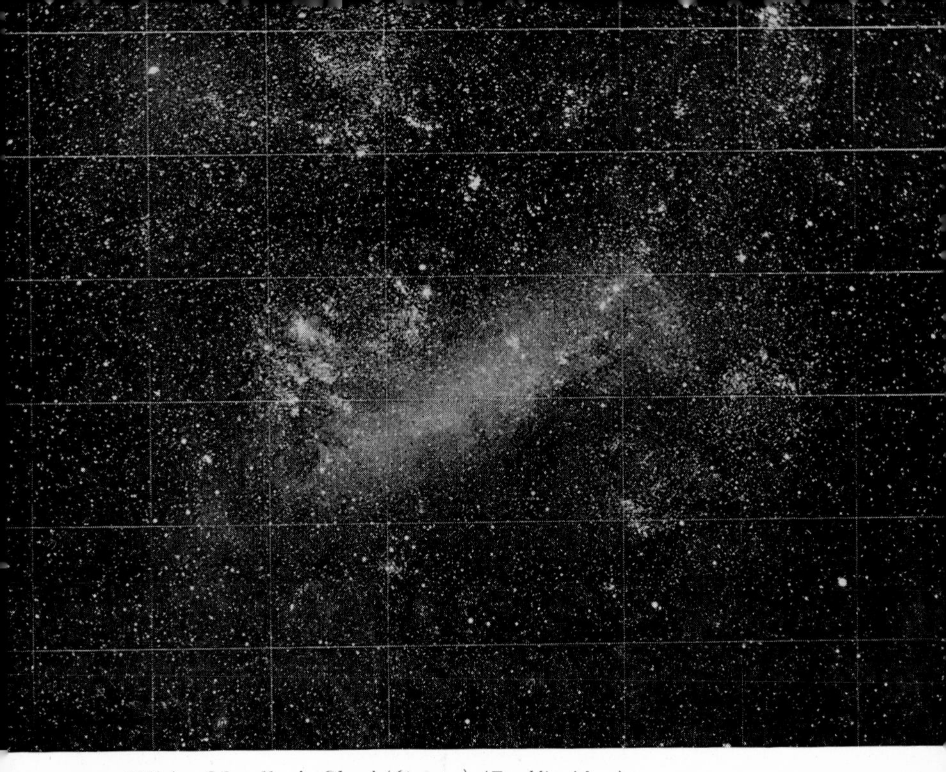

VI(a). Magellanic Cloud (Greater) (*Franklin-Adams*)

VI(b). Star Clouds in Sagittarius (*Yerkes Observatory*)

Wherein lay the inadequacy of Kelvin's calculation ? He assumed, it will be recollected, that the Sun's present condition was the result of gravitational attraction alone ; radioactivity introduced a new source of heat of which Kelvin was unaware at the time of his calculations, in addition to that arising from contraction, and consequently the age he derived for the Sun must be an underestimate. Let us consider a radioactive element such as uranium ; its atom, as we know now, consists of a massive and highly concentrated nucleus built up of 92 protons (P) and 146 neutrons (N) around which circulate 92 planetary electrons (E) as illustrated in Fig. 47. The phenomenon of radioactivity is associated with the instability of the nucleus which disintegrates spontaneously by shooting out in various stages what were originally called alpha particles—and

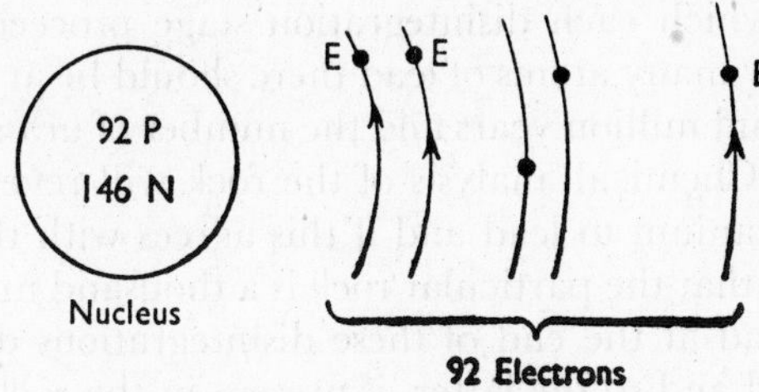

Fig. 47.—Uranium Atom

are now known to be the nuclei of helium atoms—with speeds of several thousand miles per second ; electrons and rays called gamma rays, of a penetrating power exceeding that of X-rays, are also shot out at different stages. Consider only the alpha particles ; they are soon stopped by nearby matter and their immense energy of motion is converted into heat.

If, then, the Sun contains uranium and other radioactive elements the spontaneous breaking-up of their atoms involving the release of nuclear energy provides a source of heat not envisaged in Kelvin's calculations. The rates at which the atoms of the radioactive elements disintegrate at the various stages are known and it is thus possible to calculate how much older than Kelvin's estimate the Sun must be if it contained at birth a given proportion of radioactive elements. The result is still inadequate for the claims of geology for example but, as we shall see later, the clue furnished by radioactivity as to the immense amount of energy locked up in the atomic nucleus led to revolutionary concepts as to how the Sun—and the stars—could maintain their capacity to continue as self-luminous bodies over immensely long periods of time.

Besides rendering nugatory Kelvin's calculation of the age of the Sun, radioactivity provided geology with the means of estimating accurately the ages of the rocks. We have said that uranium disintegrates in various stages ; radium, for example, represents an intermediate stage in the disintegration of the uranium atom ; the final stage of all is lead. In the transformation from uranium to lead each atom of the former shoots out eight alpha particles (or helium nuclei).

Suppose at the time of formation of the Earth's crust a sample of rock contains a million atoms of uranium ; knowing the rate at which each disintegration stage proceeds, we can calculate how many atoms of lead there should be at the end of, say, a thousand million years and the number of uranium atoms still intact. Chemical analysis of the rock will reveal the proportion of uranium to lead and if this agrees with the calculation we infer that the particular rock is a thousand million years old. The lead at the end of these disintegrations differs from ordinary lead and so the latter, if present in the rock, need not vitiate the calculation as its amount can be separately determined.

A similar calculation as to the relative amounts of uranium and helium can sometimes be achieved ; helium is, of course, a gas and does not remain enclosed within a porous rock such as sandstone ; but several kinds of rock can imprison it securely and again the age of the rock can be calculated from the ratio of the amount of uranium still unchanged to the amount of helium contained in the sample. It is easily seen that complications can arise if the rock contained another parent—such as thorium—of a similar chain of disintegrations but these complications are not unsurmountable. The age of the oldest rock found by the radioactivity-method is not far short of two thousand million years ; the age, it must be remembered, dates from the solidification of the Earth's crust. It may be added that the ages of meteorites—solid chunks of cosmic matter which occasionally fall on the Earth—range up to about three thousand million years.

We return now to our selected star Epsilon Aurigae and try to understand the physical processes responsible for its metamorphosis from a nearly non-luminous globe of vast dimensions and incredibly exiguous density to the state and condition of a luminous star. Contraction must take place at the beginning and must always *tend* to take place subsequently, simply because any atom in the star—say on its outer fringes—is attracted towards the centre of the globe according to the law of gravitation and falls a little—or tends to fall—towards the centre of the globe. As contraction proceeds the globe becomes hotter and eventually luminous. It is now a star and, as we have seen in the case of the Sun when contraction is the only physical process, it will run through the stages of its subsequent career at much too rapid a rate ; the star is, under the circumstances, using up all the available energy resulting from contraction in a time that must definitely be regarded as far too short. There must be other stores of energy on which it must draw if its life as a luminous body is to be considerably longer than that postulated by Kelvin in the case of the Sun.

Suppose now that our star has reached the stage of an M-type giant ; its surface temperature is perhaps 2500° and since heat and light are flowing out of the star the temperature must increase from the outside layers towards the star's centre. We shall further suppose that the interior temperatures are sufficiently high as to allow the star to tap some, at least, of the stores of energy which we must locate in the atom itself, for there is no other discernible source.

Previously, it was supposed that the weight of the stellar gases above a particular layer was effectively supported alone by the pressure, acting on the surface of this layer, of the gas within, but towards 1920 Sir Arthur Eddington realised that gas-pressure was aided by another, the pressure of radiation. If you hold up a hand in front of an electric light the beam of light exerts a pressure on your hand ; however, this light-pressure is so minute that you do not notice it, although its effects can be detected with very delicate apparatus. If the light-source be several hundreds of times hotter, the light-pressure, or radiation-pressure, becomes significant and within the very hot interiors of the stars it rivals gas-pressure in effectiveness.

In investigating then the equilibrium of a giant star—for, with our later ideas of the greatly extended life-time of a star, contraction is a comparatively ineffective process—Eddington introduced, first, radiation-pressure as an important factor in the internal economy of a star, second, some unspecified source of energy, and third a new factor, opacity, which means the capacity of the stellar material to slow up the passage of the radiation from the central to the outside regions.

The problem to be solved is evidently one of the greatest complexity and we can only give the briefest account of Eddington's elaborate research. If the mass of the globe with which one starts is given, then the mathematical investigation can only be successful if it can predict with reasonable accuracy a luminosity very much like that of a real star of the given mass. Consider first a globe of mass one-tenth that of the Sun ; the radiation pressure is calculated to be almost negligible compared with gas-pressure ; the " star " can, in fact, barely radiate. The inference is that real stars cannot have masses much below (if at all) one-tenth of the mass of the Sun.

At the other extreme, if the mass is a hundred times that of the Sun, radiation pressure greatly surpasses gas-pressure in importance and, although there is no precise proof, it would seem that stars with this large mass and enormous radiation pressure cannot remain as independent entities, for the radiation pressure at their surfaces is so intense that it may be expected to blow the outer fringes of the star into space, with continuous repetitions until a kind of balance is struck ; thereafter what remains of the star settles down to a normal life. It would seem then that Nature can only tolerate stars whose masses in general lie between somewhat restricted limits—say one-tenth and fifty times that of the Sun, the range within which radiation pressure and gas pressure are comparable in effectiveness.

To summarise, the theory invokes the laws of physics—including the laws of perfect gases—and predicts that if the mass is say five times the Sun's mass, the luminosity is so-and-so ; in other words, the theory arrives at a definite relationship between the mass of a giant star and its luminosity ; this is the famous mass-luminosity relationship discovered by Eddington and represented diagrammatically in Fig. 48, where the luminosity is expressed in terms of absolute magnitude. For example, the curve shows that if a star's mass is ten times that of the Sun, the corresponding point X on the diagram indicates that the absolute magnitude of the star should be about $-2{\cdot}5$ as read from the absolute magnitude scale on the left. We ask : Is the absolute magnitude of a real star of ten times the solar mass that indicated in the diagram ? In 1924 Eddington had

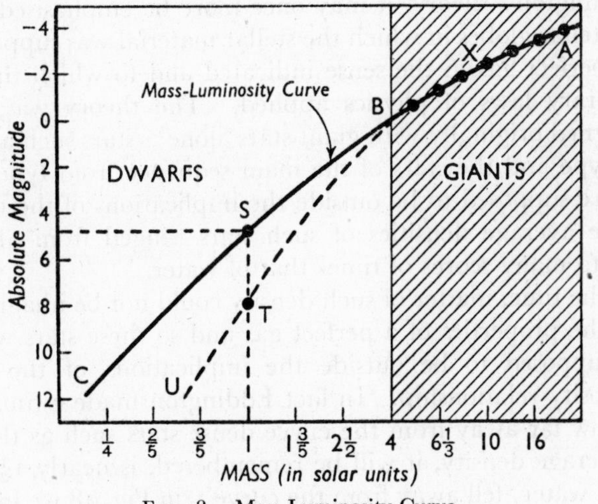

FIG. 48.—Mass-Luminosity Curve

collected reliable information pertaining to a number of giant stars and it was found that these stars conformed to the mass-luminosity relationship ; this was a notable achievement—the prediction of the luminosity of a giant star of given mass—but more was to follow.

But before proceeding to the further developments, we must emphasise one or two points. The theory was concerned with diffuse stars, that is to say, stars in which the density of stellar matter was extremely small. This matter was conceived to be a diffuse collection of atoms or molecules, to which the laws of perfect gases were applicable. Now an atom is, in a sense, a comparatively bulky entity ; it consists, as the reader will recollect, of a nucleus around which circulate a varying number of electrons ; the greater the number, the bulkier the atom. In a perfect gas—even in air—the atoms or molecules are separated by distances very many times greater than their own dimensions ; they are rushing about with velocities depending on the temperature—the greater the temperature the greater is the energy of motion of the atoms, on the average. We can now define a perfect gas, then, as one in which the atoms have very considerable freedom of motion, a mobility that is absent almost completely in a liquid and more so in a solid.

Eddington's theory, it may once more be emphasised, dealt with stellar globes in which the stellar material was supposed to be a perfect gas in the sense indicated and to which the contemporary laws of physics applied. The theory was, then, concerned originally with giant stars alone ; stars such as those of B type and the stars of the main sequence from types A to M were supposed to be outside the implications of the theory, for the average densities of such stars ranged from about a tenth to many scores of times that of water.

At the time, matter of such density could not be imagined to have the properties of a perfect gas and so these stars were at first supposed to be outside the implications of the mass-luminosity relationship. In fact Eddington made estimates of just how far away from the curve dense stars such as the Sun (its average density, it will be remembered, is nearly $1\frac{1}{2}$ times that of water) fell away from the curve ; in Fig. 48 we indicate by the broken curve BTU the anticipated curve for the dense or dwarf stars ; the Sun's position on this curve is T and reading the left-hand scale we see that its anticipated absolute magnitude is 8·2, about $3\frac{1}{2}$ magnitudes fainter than its *known* absolute magnitude. The prediction based on the current ideas of matter of a density comparable with that of water is evidently badly in error and something must be wrong in these arguments, for the Sun, as Eddington was astonished to find, conformed at S exactly to the mass-luminosity relationship (the curve ABC in Fig. 48) derived from the application of the laws of a perfect gas. Other dwarf stars of accurately measured mass and absolute magnitude conformed equally well.

There could be only one conclusion, however absurd it appeared to be ; the matter of which dwarf stars, such as the Sun, are fabricated must be in the state of a perfect gas. But how could this be when one thinks of their densities in many cases greatly exceeding that of water and even that of the densest terrestrial elements ? And the situation appeared even more absurd when one considered the density of the stellar material in the central regions of dwarf stars, which apparently—if the mass-luminosity relationship applied to them—might be hundreds of times the density of water.

The absurdity was removed when the state of atoms within a star, dwarf or giant, is considered in the light of ionisation. Consider the Sun as a typical dwarf star. The central temperature—as we shall see—is calculated to be about 20 million degrees. At this temperature no atomic structure can remain intact ; the single electron of the normal * hydrogen atom is expelled and instead of one entity—namely, the complete atom —we have two discrete particles, one a proton and the other an electron, rushing about the interior of the star as independent units. Take a more complicated element such as copper ; the normal atom consists of a nucleus and 29 planetary electrons ; if all these electrons are removed by ionisation, there are now 30 independent particles roaming within the star—namely, 1 nucleus and 29 electrons.

Moreover the nucleus and electron are infinitesimal in size compared with the relatively bulky atom of which they were constituents originally ; consequently, the mobility of nuclei and electrons even when they are compressed a million-fold is no whit inferior to the mobility of atoms (or molecules) in ordinary air or within the deep recesses of a giant star even if it be assumed that there the atoms remain intact. We can thus pack into a given volume of the star a mass of independent nuclei and electrons a million times greater than we could do, if the atoms remained intact, without sacrificing the conception of a perfect gas.

At this point the question of the chemical constitution of the star arises, for it would seem impossible to bring under one

* Used as a term relating to ordinary terrestrial conditions when the atoms have their full quota of planetary electrons.

generalisation—the mass-luminosity relationship—stars of diverse chemical composition. Again, ionisation comes to the rescue to effect a remarkable simplification. In the laws of a perfect gas we are concerned with the *average* weight of the gaseous constituents. It is convenient for our purpose to take the weight of a proton (the nucleus of the hydrogen atom) to be unit weight; further, the weight of an electron is only 1/1840 of the weight of a proton and, practically, is of negligible account when we calculate the average weights of *all* the particles in a stellar gas. We have just seen that a copper atom, if completely ionised, is reduced to 30 independent particles (1 nucleus and 29 electrons); in terms of our unit the weight of the copper nucleus is known to be 63½ and, consequently, the *average* weight of the 30 particles (ignoring the weight of the electrons) is 63½ divided by 30 or about 2·1.

If we consider in the same way the heaviest of all the elements, uranium, its nucleus is 238 times the weight of the proton and around it circulate 92 electrons; if the atom is completely ionised, there will be 93 independent particles and the average weight of the particles will be 238 divided by 93 or about 2·5. Next to hydrogen and helium the lightest element is lithium; the weight of its nucleus is 7, and as the atom has three planetary electrons the number of independent particles arising from the complete ionisation of the atom is 4; the *average* weight of these particles is 1¾. If we assume for the moment that hydrogen and helium do not form a significant proportion of the constituents of a star, it is evident that the average weight of a particle in a star built up mainly of the remaining elements lies between 1¾ and 2½ and, on any reasonable combination of such elements, the average weight of a particle is about $2\frac{1}{10}$ times the weight of a proton—the value adopted by Eddington in his earlier investigations.

With the proviso mentioned, it appears that, in any preliminary survey, the chemical composition of a star is hardly likely to be important, for the essential item in applying the laws of a perfect gas—the average weight of a particle—is known with substantial accuracy. This represented an immense simplification in solving the problem of the physical constitution of a star in its broad outline, one of the principal results being the mass-luminosity relationship. It may be added that this relationship enables us to derive the mass of any main-sequence star if its luminosity—or absolute magnitude—is known; for we simply mark the point on the curve corresponding to the given absolute magnitude and then the appropriate reading on the horizontal scale* gives us the mass.

Eddington's investigations also led to an evaluation of the central temperature and density for a main-sequence star of given characteristics, but these have now to be modified in the light of the more recently acquired knowledge that hydrogen is the most abundant element in the universe and forms a considerable proportion by weight of an average star. Our preceding account was based on the qualification that hydrogen and helium were not abundant in a star.

Consider first an ionised hydrogen atom disrupted into two independent particles, one a proton (of unit weight) and the other an electron (of negligible weight); the average weight of the two particles is thus $\frac{1}{2}$, far removed from the average weight of $2\frac{1}{10}$ which we found earlier for a representative chemical composition of the elements from lithium to uranium. Similarly, an ionised helium atom, with a nucleus of weight four, will yield three independent particles—two are electrons—and the average weight of these particles is $1\frac{1}{3}$, again well-removed from the value of $2\frac{1}{10}$. It is then evident that we shall get different results for the central temperature, in particular, according to the hydrogen—and to a lesser extent the helium-—content in a star. For example, if the star is made of hydrogen alone, its central temperature is found to be about ten million degrees, while if it is made of a mixture of the heavier elements such as iron its temperature is about four times higher.

The internal temperatures of a star play a very important part, as we shall see, in providing a clue to the method whereby energy is released within a star and as the central temperature depends on the relative abundance of hydrogen—and, to a lesser extent, of helium—the chemical composition is now seen to play a rather more important role than was envisaged by Eddington in his earlier researches. Further, the nature of the

* The horizontal scale in Fig. 48 is given, for convenience, in terms of the logarithms of the masses; hence its apparent peculiarity.

chemical composition affects another factor in the problem, namely, the opacity of the stellar material which we mentioned on page 132 and which regulates the rate of flow of energy from the centre of the star to its surface ; for example, helium has a greater blanketing effect on the outward-flowing radiation than hydrogen, and of two stars, one with a large helium content and the other with a similarly large hydrogen content, the central temperature of the former will be higher than that of the latter.

In applying theoretical principles to the elucidation of the physical properties of a star such as the Sun, we note that we have three " observables " at our disposal, namely (i) the solar mass, (ii) the solar radius and (iii) the Sun's luminosity, which can be described as the rate at which radiant energy is being emitted into space—this rate, it is to be remarked, is the same as that at which energy is released within the star. The object of the theoretical investigator is to deduce from the laws of physics how the temperature and density vary from the surface towards the centre, using the observables (i) and (ii) and assuming a given proportion of hydrogen and of the heavier elements—in this explanation we can omit, for simplicity, any reference to helium. From his calculations he can derive the luminosity of the Sun and if this agrees with the observable (iii) he has been fortunate in his guess as to the chemical constitution.

More likely, the Sun's calculated luminosity will be found to be different from the observed luminosity and he must guess again and repeat his calculations until the calculated and observed luminosities agree. The problem is evidently a very complex one and becomes still more difficult when helium is introduced as a constituent of the solar material.

The hydrogen content of many stars, investigated in this way, is found to be very considerable ; for example, the chemical constitution of the Sun is such that one-third of the total mass of our luminary is hydrogen and the remainder consists mainly of the heavier elements—other than helium, of which the proportion is believed to be small. With this chemical constitution the central temperature of the Sun is calculated to be about twenty million degrees and the central density about

110 times that of water. There is not, as might be expected, complete unanimity as to the central temperatures of representative stars of the main-sequence derived from calculations of the kind described, but taking round figures we are not likely to be far from the truth in suggesting that the central temperatures vary progressively from about ten million degrees for red dwarfs (of type M) to about thirty-five million degrees for the hot stars of type O.

We now return to the problem of stellar evolution and, in particular, to the mechanism by which a star contrives to tap energy in such a way as to maintain its status as a luminous body over great expanses of time. Gravitational contraction, by itself, has been shown to be inadequate as an energy-providing process and so we have to look further afield. One process suggested at one time is related to radioactivity. Suppose a star had a large uranium content ; the uranium nucleus is unstable and sooner or later, as we have seen, an alpha-particle (the nucleus of helium) is shot out with a speed of several thousand miles per second ; the energy of motion of the particle is converted into heat. We know the rate at which uranium atoms disintegrate ; of two million uranium atoms one million will remain intact—that is, unchanged—after 4600 million years ; the process is thus a slow one and even although the subsequent series of disintegrations, culminating eventually in the production of lead, are more rapid the rate at which heat is produced proves insufficient for the metamorphosis of a globe of uranium atoms into a body of the luminosity of the Sun. In recent years radioactive elements of greater weight than uranium have been artificially produced—such as neptunium and plutonium—but to assume that such elements, with much greater heat-producing actions than uranium, are constituents of the Sun merely solves one problem at the expense of creating another.

If uranium is to be regarded as a necessary agent in the production of energy within the stars, a much more drastic release of energy than that provided by the spontaneous disintegration of uranium nuclei is found in the process which gave birth to the atomic bomb. We have said that the uranium nucleus is naturally unstable ; this readiness to explode is immensely enhanced when a neutron is fired into the nucleus, for then the augmented nucleus breaks up into roughly equal portions which fly apart with great velocity, the energy of motion being transformed into heat-energy by collision with other atoms. The requirements, then, as regards this suggestion are a plentiful supply, within the deep recesses of the stars, of uranium and of neutrons moving with sufficient speed to enable them to penetrate the uranium nuclei. The first requirement is inconsistent with our knowledge of the relatively small proportion of uranium in the material make-up of the universe ; consequently, it would seem that any argument purporting to explain the release of energy within the stars, based on the radioactive elements, must fail to carry conviction.

About a quarter of a century ago when a great amount of observational data had been accumulated, it was noticed—as we have remarked on page 127—that there was, in general, a progressive decrease in mass from the giant red stars of type M to the stars of type B and from the latter, along the main sequence, to dwarf red stars of type M. On Russell's theory of evolution this must mean that the stars got rid of a large proportion of their mass as they proceeded along the evolutionary route. By Einstein's principle of the equivalence of mass and energy (page 125), the rate at which mass is being lost can be calculated, say, in the case of the Sun and, further, the intervals required by the Sun to diminish from two, three, or more solar masses to its present mass can be found. These intervals are enormous ; for example, if the Sun started its evolutionary career as a diffuse globe of twenty times its present mass the interval required amounts to about seven million million years—an interval which may be conveniently described as the "age" of the Sun ; it may be added that the age turns out to be little different if the Sun's initial mass were only, say, ten times its present mass.

It is evident, then, that Russell's evolutionary progression can also be described on the whole as a progression in ages, the giant red stars being the youngest and the dwarf red stars the oldest. To explain how matter could be converted into radiation—the process by which a star is daily losing mass—it was supposed that collisions of protons, for example, with electrons in the deep interior of a star resulted in a splash of radiant energy equivalent, according to Einstein's principle, to the mass of the particles concerned. The " annihilation of matter ", as the process was described, has never been observed in the laboratory and although in more recent times the mutual destruction of electrons and positrons (of the same character as electrons, except that they carry positive charges) is a commonplace, the " annihilation-theory " lost favour for various reasons despite the fact that it gave astronomers almost unlimited time to play with.

One reason related to the difficulty of explaining the coexistence, in a binary system, of a " young " star and an " old " star. A further compelling reason is concerned with the theory of the expanding universe, a theory which assigns ages to the stars of several thousand million years and no more. If the ages of the stars are as suggested, Russell's theory of stellar evolution, however grandiose in conception and satisfying in many ways, must be discarded. It follows that the evolution of a star is distinctly limited ; it is born, so to speak, at or near the point in the Hertzsprung-Russell diagram corresponding to its present position there, its mass at birth being just a very little greater than it is at present.

Through the rapid advances of atomic physics between the two world-wars new ideas were applied to the problem of the generation of energy within a star, based essentially on the accurate determination of atomic weights, the application of Einstein's principle and the transmutation of the elements by bombardment with fast-moving alpha particles, protons or neutrons. We have previously referred (page 139) to the disintegration of uranium nuclei by means of neutrons—a process discovered in the laboratory only as late as 1939.

One of the earliest transmutations, accompanied by a relatively large release of energy, occurred in the bombardment of lithium by protons, the experimenters being Sir John Cockcroft and Professor E. T. S. Walton, then members of the Cavendish Laboratory staff at Cambridge. The lithium nucleus consists of 3 protons (P) and 4 neutrons (N) as indicated in Fig. 49 (*a*), the nucleus carrying a positive electric charge of three units (the unit being the charge on a proton). The lithium atom itself consists of the nucleus and three planetary electrons, the dimensions of the atom as a whole being vastly greater than the dimensions of the nucleus and the electrons. Consequently, if a particle such as a proton is fired with great speed at an atom the chances are that it will pass through the empty spaces of the atom leaving the latter unaffected.

But occasionally a proton will make a direct hit on the nucleus and, if its speed is sufficiently great, it will become embedded, so to speak, in the nucleus which will now consist of 4 protons and 4 neutrons, as indicated in Fig. 49 (*b*) ; it is to be remarked that the bombarding proton must be launched with great speed so as to overcome the electrical repulsion between the posi-

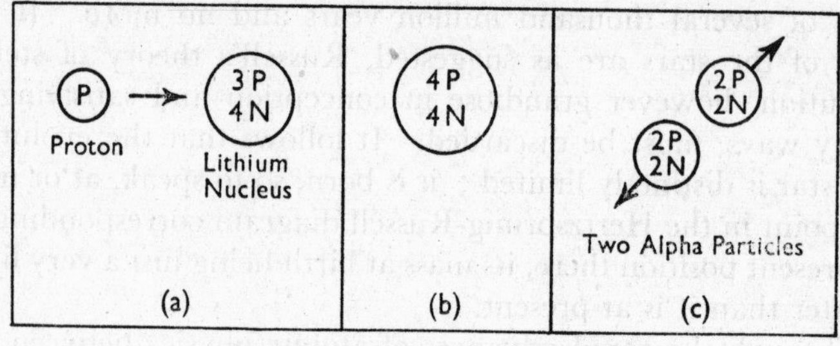

FIG. 49.—Bombardment of Lithium

tively charged lithium nucleus and the positively charged proton. The new nucleus, Fig. 49(*b*), is unstable and it immediately disintegrates, as shown in Fig. 49 (*c*), into two alpha particles (or helium nuclei) which fly apart with immense speeds. The energy of motion of the two alpha particles is soon converted into heat through collisions with other atoms. The energy thus produced must come from the hidden store of energy locked up in the lithium nucleus. A rough calculation, based on Einstein's principle, will show the relative proportion of energy released in the bombardment. For reasons we need not particularise the unit weight applied to atoms is based on the atomic weight of oxygen and in terms of this unit the atomic weights of all the elements have been measured with very great accuracy by the late Dr. F. W. Aston at Cambridge, with an instrument called the mass-spectrograph, and by later investigators. For our purpose we can take the weights of the proton (P), alpha particle (A), and lithium nucleus (L) to be, with sufficient accuracy, as follows :

P, 1·008 : A, 4·004 : L, 7·018.

The weight of the combined nucleus in Fig. 49 (*b*) is then

7·018 + 1·008, or 8·026.

The weight of the two alpha particles in Fig. 49 (*c*) is twice 4·004, or 8·008. The explosion of the combined nucleus thus results in a loss of weight given by 8·026 – 8·008, that is 0·018 or very roughly 2 per cent. of the weight of a proton ; omitting one or two minor considerations, this loss of weight is, by Einstein's principle, equivalent to the energy of motion of the two alpha particles. The successful bombardment of lithium is, then, a process whereby mass is converted into one of the more familiar forms of energy.

In a similar way the nuclei of the lighter elements can be transformed by bombardment with protons.

There is one point of importance, however, to notice when we apply the principles of nuclear bombardment to the release of energy within the stars. In the case of lithium we have said that the speed of the protons required for the penetration of the nucleus must be such as to overcome, in the first instance, the electric repulsion between the nucleus and the proton. If we consider the bombardment of a nucleus of the next heavier element, beryllium, the electric repulsion is greater than in the case of lithium, for the beryllium nucleus consists of 4 protons and 5 neutrons and has consequently a positive charge of 4 units, as opposed to 3 units for lithium.

For the next heavier elements, in order, the positive charges are 5 for boron, 6 for carbon, 7 for nitrogen and so on, so that the electric repulsion between the nuclei and the bombarding proton increases as we proceed from lighter to heavier elements and this implies that we must use faster protons for a heavier element than for a lighter, if transmutation is to occur. Now temperature at a point within a star is an index of the average speed of the constituent particles there ; in particular, the higher the temperature the greater is the speed of protons. It is clear that if nuclear transformations, of the kind described, occur within the stars then there is an appropriate temperature associated with each element, and this temperature is greater for a heavier element than for a lighter.

We have mentioned the bombardment by protons of the lighter elements lithium and so on to nitrogen, and we ask what happens if we bombard the nuclei of the two lightest elements, hydrogen and helium, with protons ? Taking helium first, the nucleus is a tightly-bound structure impervious to the assaults of protons travelling even with great speeds ; it is, in fact, usually one of the products of the nuclear transformation of the heavier elements and within the stars the helium content steadily increases. In the case of the bombardment of protons by protons the nucleus of what is called an *isotope* of hydrogen (named deuterium) is formed with the expulsion of a positron, and this nucleus is given the special name of *deuteron* ; the deuteron consists of one proton and one neutron and, therefore, like the proton carries unit positive charge. It may be added that the expelled positron soon encounters an electron and the result is a splash of radiation, that is, energy. Deuterons themselves are exposed to further bombardment by protons and in this case the nucleus of a lighter isotope of helium is formed, consisting of two protons and one neutron.

We are now in a position to trace—to some extent, at least—the development of a diffuse gaseous star such as Epsilon Aurigae through successive stages. The gaseous globe contracts and becomes hotter ; contraction is only arrested when the temperature is sufficiently high to allow a nuclear transmutation to become operative in releasing energy. At this stage when the central temperature is about half a million degrees the nuclear transmutation is supposed to be the conversion of deuterons into the light isotope of helium. The star adjusts itself to the ensuing temperature changes and when the supply of the deuterons is exhausted it begins to contract once more and consequently to become still hotter. At a temperature of about 4 or 5 million degrees the lithium transmutation begins to be effective, resulting in still higher temperatures and an increase in the luminosity of the star. On the exhaustion of lithium, contraction occurs once more followed by an increase

VII. Great Nebula in Andromeda
(*Yerkes Observatory*)

VIII. Group of Extragalactic Nebulae in Leo
(*Mt. Wilson Observatory*)

in temperature when the transmutation of another of the lighter elements begins.

In the case of the Sun, in which the central temperature is about twenty million degrees, a much more complicated process, discovered by Dr. Bethe of Cornell University, takes charge in drawing on nuclear energy to maintain the Sun's prodigal outpouring of heat and light. It must be understood, of course, that before reaching its present condition the Sun must have exhausted what supplies of deuteron, lithium and one or two of the lighter elements it had in its earlier days. Bethe's process, known as the carbon-nitrogen cycle, is as follows, the necessary conditions being a temperature of about twenty million degrees—or rather less—and an adequate supply of carbon or nitrogen or both. The cycle occurs in six stages.

In the first stage, a carbon nucleus is bombarded by a proton which, to use our phraseology, becomes embedded in the nucleus ; as the original carbon nucleus consists of 6 protons and 6 neutrons, the new nucleus is compounded of 7 protons and 6 neutrons and is, in fact, a radioactive isotope of nitrogen.

In the second stage this nucleus shoots out a positron and becomes the nucleus of the heavy isotope of carbon consisting of 6 protons and 7 neutrons—it is just as if one of the protons got rid of its positive charge by the expulsion of the positron and became a neutron.

The third stage is the bombardment of the heavy carbon nucleus by a fast-moving proton ; at the end of this stage the nucleus consists now of 7 protons and 7 neutrons and is the nucleus of the ordinary nitrogen atom.

In the fourth stage the nitrogen nucleus captures another proton, becoming now the nucleus of the lighter isotope of oxygen with 8 protons and 7 neutrons ; this isotope is unstable and, in the fifth stage, it is transformed by the process described in the second stage into a nucleus of 7 protons and 8 neutrons with the expulsion of a positron ; this latter nucleus is a nucleus of the heavier isotope of nitrogen.

The final stage is the bombardment of this nucleus by yet another fast-moving proton the result of which is the disintegration into a carbon nucleus, of the same constitution as that with which we started, and a helium nucleus. At several stages, it should be added, energy of short-wave length (called "gamma rays") is also emitted.

It is to be noticed that in the first three stages the proton-bombardment of ordinary carbon results in the production of ordinary nitrogen ; in the remaining stages the ordinary nitrogen is converted into ordinary carbon ; it is evident then that we can describe the cycle equally well as beginning with the bombardment of nitrogen.

The process can succinctly be described as follows : we start with a certain amount of carbon in the deep interior of the star ; then follows a series of bombardments of a carbon nucleus and its successive forms by four protons ; the results are (i) the restoration of the carbon nucleus and (ii) the production of a helium nucleus ; effectively, then, hydrogen has been transformed into helium. Omitting the energy emitted in the form of positrons and gamma rays we can calculate by Einstein's principle the amount of energy released in the cycle ; the mass of 4 protons is 4 times 1·008, or 4·032 ; the mass of the helium nucleus produced is 4·004 ; the series of transformations results then in a loss of 4·032 – 4·004 units of mass, that is 0·028 units, and this appears as radiant energy. Moreover, the rate at which the conversion of hydrogen into helium occurs can be calculated from the various factors that enter into the problem and this rate must be substantially the observed rate at which the Sun pours out heat and light into space—we can omit as negligible the contribution provided by the transmutation of the surviving lighter elements such as lithium near the surface of the Sun where the temperature is favourable for such transmutations.

As we have seen, most of the nuclear processes result in the formation of helium—in the case of the carbon-nitrogen cycle, helium is built up from the lighter element hydrogen, and in the case of the lithium process, for example, a heavier element (lithium) is converted into a lighter one (helium). Further, Bethe's cycle presupposes that still heavier elements, carbon and nitrogen, are already in existence within the solar globe. At one time it was thought that all the elements had been fabricated out of hydrogen in the immensely hot interiors of the stars, but it would now seem that such a suggestion is incompatible with present-day views as to the source of stellar energy. The inference is that in a globe of primordial matter, a state to which the giant Epsilon Aurigae approximates, the elements in the whole range from hydrogen to uranium are already in existence, and if we try to explain, for example, the compounding of an uranium nucleus out of 92 protons and 146 neutrons we seem to be led back to the misty past of the material universe before the stars were born.

The nuclear processes which we have described have proved successful in the general problem of locating the source of energy in the main-sequence stars as a whole, an issue of fundamental importance. Nuclear physics is a young science and it can hardly be expected that we have glimpsed more than just a few of the secrets of stellar economy. Our main topic of stellar evolution, however, appears to be less obscure than it was a quarter of a century ago. The stars evolve by consuming their hydrogen content—either at the expense of the lighter elements such as lithium or in the mechanism of the carbon-nitrogen cycle—at the same time adding to their store of helium. An accretion of helium results in the slower transference of radiation from a stellar interior to its surface, which in turn suggests that the star will become hotter with a still more rapid release of energy by nuclear processes so long as hydrogen is in plentiful supply. There must come a time when the available hydrogen becomes insufficient to maintain the luminosity of the star at its highest level : the star must diminish in luminosity and when the store of hydrogen is exhausted gravitational attraction remains as the only source of energy.

Chapter VI

DELTA CEPHEI, A PULSATING STAR

In a previous chapter we have considered eclipsing variable stars which it is well to remember are, in general, normal binary stars ; because of adventitious geometrical conditions, such stars appear to vary in brightness as the result of the mutual eclipses of the components. Indeed, there is nothing remarkable as a rule about the individual components and if the binary formations were broken up and the components dispersed in all directions, such individuals would be indistinguishable from the vast majority of the stars in the stellar system. In the present chapter we describe a totally different type of variable star which owes the changes in brightness to physical causes peculiar to the star itself. The prototype of this new type of variable is the third magnitude star Delta Cephei which gives its name to the class as a whole known as *cepheids*. At first sight cepheid variation might be expected to be little more than an interesting phenomenon unrelated to any of the major problems of astronomy ; perhaps it is well to state at the outset that without the assistance of cepheids we would have found it difficult, if not impossible, to obtain a reliable estimate of the vast extent of the visible universe which is part of the astronomical knowledge of the present time.

The position of Delta Cephei is shown in the star-map in Fig. 50.

In Chapter II we were concerned with the laborious operation of measuring the distance of an individual star by the fundamental method of direct surveying. With the large telescopes devoted to this exacting work it is possible to sound space with reasonable accuracy to a depth of perhaps 500 light-years ; if we try to measure the distance of a star actually 1000 light-years away, the best we can do is to obtain a result which, in round numbers, makes it reasonably probable that the star's distance is somewhere between 500 and 2000 light-years. It is evident that the surveyor's method is severely limited in sounding space and consequently other methods must be sought in our explorations beyond the immediate neighbourhood of the Sun.

One such method is based on the Hertzsprung-Russell diagram with which we were concerned in the previous chapter (page 121). We illustrate the application of the method with reference to stellar formations known as "open clusters"; these are aggregations of stars occupying a comparatively small volume of space and too far away for the surveying-method to be successful in furnishing their distances. It will be assumed

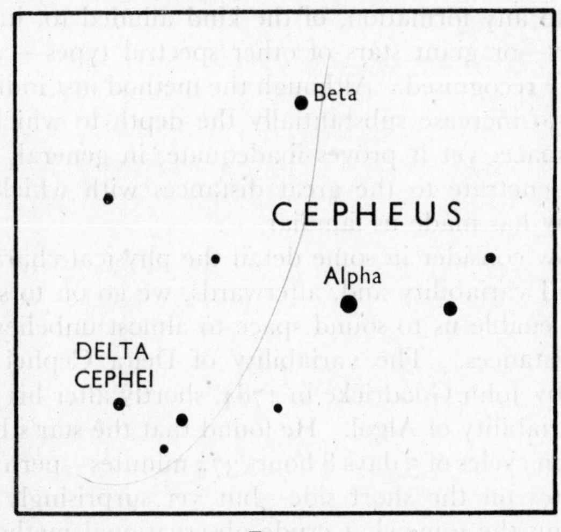

Fig. 50

that the spectra of the brightest stars in the cluster are known; if some of these are of B type then the Hertzsprung-Russell diagram enables us to specify the absolute magnitudes of the stars concerned. For example, if we have stars belonging to a particular sub-division of B type we find from the diagram that the absolute magnitude is $-1{\cdot}5$, say. The apparent magnitude of these stars can be readily obtained by one of the usual methods; if these turn out, on the average to be $+8{\cdot}5$, say, a simple calculation then shows the distance of these stars is about 3200 light-years; if, as we have assumed, the formation is compact this distance is in effect the distance of the cluster itself. If some of the brightest stars are of M type these are almost certain to be red giants—possibly verifiable as such by examination of the spectra, for there are certain comparatively minute differences between the spectra of red giants and red dwarfs—and again the information supplied by the Hertzsprung-Russell diagram enables us, as in the case of the B type stars, to deduce the distance of the cluster.

Although there are complications in the application of the method arising from the dimming effect of the interstellar cloud or " fog ", to which we shall refer in more detail in Chapter VIII, yet the general principles described can be applied to any formation, of the kind alluded to, in which B type stars—or giant stars of other spectral types—can be individually recognised. Although the method just indicated enables us to increase substantially the depth to which we can explore space, yet it proves inadequate, in general, when we seek to penetrate to the great distances with which modern astronomy has made us familiar.

We now consider in some detail the physical characteristics of cepheid variability and, afterwards, we go on to show how cepheids enable us to sound space to almost unbelievably immense distances. The variability of Delta Cephei was discovered by John Goodricke in 1784, shortly after his discovery of the variability of Algol. He found that the star's brightness changed in cycles of 5 days 8 hours 37½ minutes—perhaps about 10 minutes on the short side—but yet surprisingly accurate considering the somewhat crude observational methods at his disposal. In one of his papers to the Royal Society he wrote, referring to the three variable stars he had discovered, " such enquiries may probably lead to some better knowledge of the fixed stars especially of their constitution and the cause of their remarkable changes ". Modern research has justified—and more than justified—the instinctive faith of the young astronomer that his discoveries were only the prelude to a clearer understanding of the heavenly bodies.

With modern equipment the light-curve of Delta Cephei can be accurately obtained ; Fig. 51 shows the light-curve based on observations made by the author and Mr. H. E. Green in 1935 with the photoelectric equipment of Cambridge

Observatory. The curve shows that the change of brightness is continuous; from the maximum at A the star diminishes steadily in brightness to the minimum at B (about a magnitude fainter than at A) taking about 3 days 19 hours; from B the rise in brightness to maximum at C is comparatively rapid, the time being about 1 day 13½ hours. The period of the light-changes—that is, the interval between A and C—is 5 days 8

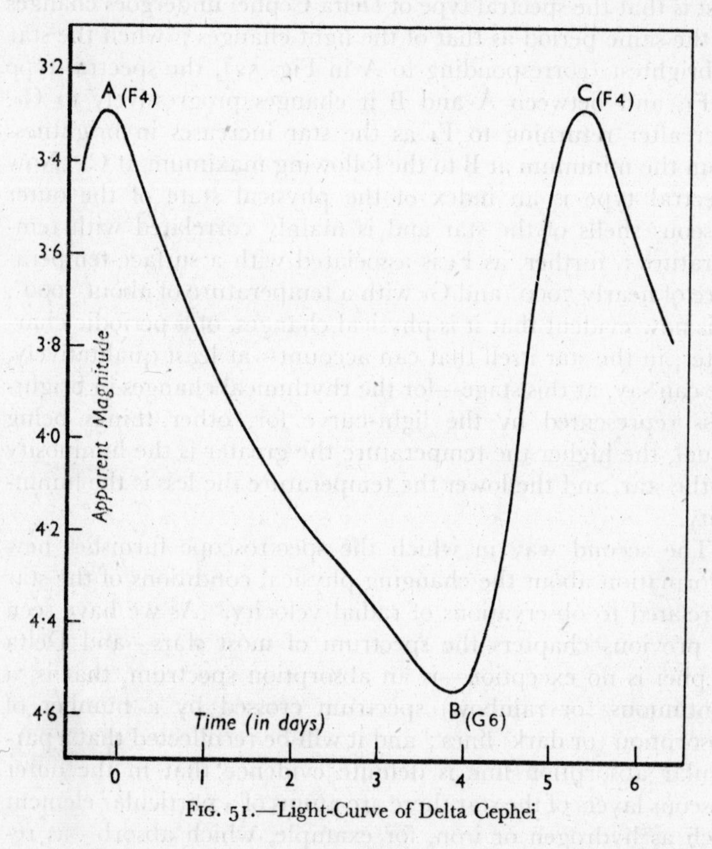

FIG. 51.—Light-Curve of Delta Cephei

hours 47 minutes 27 seconds, which is accurate to within one or two seconds. The character of the curve is totally different from the light-curve of an eclipsing variable such as is shown in Fig. 34 (page 100): consequently there would be little justification in attempting to relate the changes in brightness of the star to causes even remotely connected with the eclipse phenomena associated with such a star as Algol. Some other interpretation must be sought and for this purpose we require other observational evidence different in character from that furnished by the changes in brightness.

It is not surprising, then, that appeal is made to the spectroscope which provides information of two different kinds. The first is that the spectral type of Delta Cephei undergoes changes in the same period as that of the light changes; when the star is brightest (corresponding to A in Fig. 52), the spectral type is F_4, and between A and B it changes progressively to G_6, thereafter returning to F_4 as the star increases in brightness from the minimum at B to the following maximum at C. Now spectral type is an index of the physical state of the outer gaseous shells of the star and is mainly correlated with temperature; further, as F_4 is associated with a surface-temperature of nearly 7000° and G_6 with a temperature of about 5000°, it is now evident that it is physical changes, of a periodic character, in the star itself that can account—at least qualitatively, we can say, at this stage—for the rhythmical changes in brightness represented by the light-curve for, other things being equal, the higher the temperature the greater is the luminosity of the star, and the lower the temperature the less is the luminosity.

The second way in which the spectroscope furnishes new information about the changing physical conditions of the star is related to observations of radial velocity. As we have seen in previous chapters the spectrum of most stars—and Delta Cephei is no exception—is an absorption spectrum, that is, a continuous (or rainbow) spectrum crossed by a number of absorption (or dark) lines; and it will be recollected that a particular absorption line is definite evidence that in the outer gaseous layers of the star there are atoms of a particular element such as hydrogen or iron, for example, which absorb—as regards one or more definite wave-lengths—the radiation issuing outwards from the inner photospheric regions of the star, the latter radiation being in fact the source of the continuous spectrum. We have seen further, referring to Fig. 41, page 106, that if the star is moving towards us the wave-length of a particular absorption line as measured in the spectrum is a little less than the wave-length measured in the laboratory ; in this event we say that the line is displaced towards the violet end of the spectrum and, further, by measuring the displacement we can deduce that the star is moving towards us with such and such a velocity, expressed in miles per second ; this is the star's radial velocity of approach. In the same way, if the star is moving away from us, any absorption line is displaced towards the red end of the spectrum and again by measuring the displacement we can deduce the star's radial velocity of recession.

In the case of a normal single star the displacement of a particular absorption line remains the same from day to day and from year to year, which simply means that the star is approaching us, or receding from us, as the case may be, at a constant rate. A series of spectra of Delta Cephei, secured at intervals of an hour or two, reveal characteristic differences from the spectra to which we have just alluded. The measurement of the absorption lines shows unmistakably that the lines undergo periodic displacements, the period being the same as that of the light-curve ; when we convert these displacements in terms of radial velocity it is found that the radial velocity of the star's outer layers varies between a velocity of recession of 5 miles per second to a velocity of approach of a little over 23 miles per second.

Since we can rule out the possibility that Delta Cephei is other than a single star, the variation in radial velocity derived from the spectra of the star cannot be attributed to peculiarities in the motion of the star as a whole, for it would be fantastic to suppose that a single stellar unit, remote from all influences, should behave—to take a rather artificial example—like a runner on a straight track who is, for some reason or other, accelerating and decelerating his motion in a perfectly rhythmical way. The only explanation fitting the facts is that the star is expanding and contracting in a regular manner ; when it is expanding, the outer atmospheric layers from which the absorption lines are derived are rushing towards us with a velocity which is a combination of (i) the velocity of approach of the star as a whole which, from the data above, we can take to be 9 miles per second and (ii) the velocity of expansion of the outer gaseous layers with reference to the star's centre. Similarly when the star is contracting, the observed velocity derived from the absorption lines is a combination of (i) above and

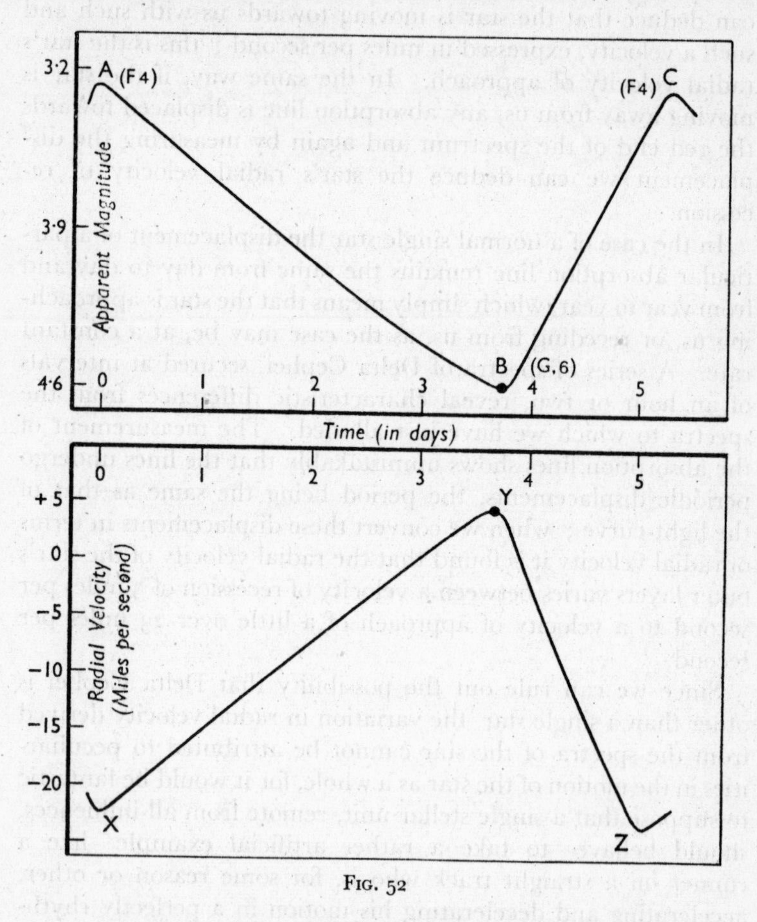

FIG. 52

(ii) the velocity with which the gaseous layers are falling towards the star's centre. The explanation, then, is that the star *pulsates*, alternately expanding and contracting in a fixed period, identical with that of the light-changes.

The changes in velocity can be represented by a " velocity curve " which is related to the light-curve as indicated in

Fig. 52; in the top half the light-curve from Fig. 51 is reproduced and the velocity curve (XYZ) is given in the lower part, a velocity of recession being denoted by + and a velocity of approach by −. It is found that when the star is brightest (at A) the greatest velocity of recession occurs almost simultaneously at X, and at minimum on the light-curve (at B) the greatest velocity of approach occurs almost simultaneously at Y. The spectral types at maximum and minimum are indicated, for reference, in the upper part of the diagram.

We consider now the luminosity of Delta Cephei. Attempts to derive its distance by the fundamental method show that the star is beyond the limit of distance for any really accurate measurement. As the star is of the third apparent magnitude it is evident that it is of great luminosity and, as will be seen later, an accurate measurement of its luminosity (and of other cepheids) is essential when we consider the role of these stars in carrying our exploration of space to great distances. There are about a dozen cepheids visible to the naked eye—it is of interest to note that the Pole-star is a cepheid with a period of just under 4 days and a range in brightness of about one-twelfth of a magnitude.

Since the direct method of distance-measurement in any individual instance is unproductive of accurate results, a statistical method is employed based on the observed proper motions of the cepheids, the details of which we pass over. It is then found by a variety of considerations that Delta Cephei, for example, is about 600 light-years distant, that is, it is a giant star about 660 times more luminous on the average than the Sun (its luminosity of course varies during the period of light-changes), that its average radius is about 12 million miles (27 times the Sun's radius), that its mass is about $10\frac{1}{2}$ times the Sun's mass, and that its average density is about 1/1250 times that of water.

The pulsation theory of the cepheids was first suggested independently by H. C. Plummer and H. Shapley about the time of the first world war, followed a few years later by Eddington's celebrated mathematical researches. Although the pulsation theory has not yet accounted for every detail in the very difficult problem of interpreting the phenomena of cepheid-variation, yet it is generally agreed that no other explanation can fit the main facts.

One important result emerging from Eddington's researches is a relation between the period and the average density of a cepheid. Other relations have been established; first, the average spectral type (average, that is, during the characteristic period of light and other changes of the individual cepheid) is clearly related to period, as shown below:

Period (in days)	$\frac{1}{2}$	4	8	20
Average spectral type	A	F5	G0	G5

A second relationship is that between period and average radius.

We consider now the variables of cepheid type in distant stellar formations. As far back as 1895, Bailey of Harvard discovered a large number of variable stars in several globular clusters; about a hundred of such clusters are known. As Plate V (b) (facing page 128) shows, these are immense aggregations of stars from a hundred thousand to a million in number—and possibly very many more, since the feebler dwarf stars, if present, are not sufficiently luminous to show up in direct photographs. In the majority of cases the period of light variation of the variables was round about half a day and the light-curves were of the characteristic cepheid type; these stars were—and are still—referred to as *cluster-variables* but this distinction in nomenclature is now generally regarded as a somewhat arbitrary one on the whole; however, we can retain the division and say that cluster variables are characterised by periods of less than one day and cepheids by periods exceeding one day.

In 1912 Miss Leavitt (also of Harvard) made a significant discovery relating to variable stars of cepheid type observed photographically in the Lesser Magellanic Cloud in the southern sky, so called after the famous Portuguese navigator Magellan who, in the Magellan Straits, has left his name also in terrestrial geography. As we now know, the Lesser Magellanic Cloud, as well as the Greater Cloud—see Plate VI (a) (facing page 129)—is an independent stellar system—on a much smaller scale, however, than the Galactic System of which the Sun is a member—at a distance of about 84,000 light-years. Accordingly, we can suppose without any significant error that all the stars in the Cloud are at the same distance from us.

A photograph of the Cloud will then enable us to grade the stars according to luminosity although, in the absence of any knowledge of the Cloud's distance, we are unable to specify the intrinsic brightness of any star in terms of the Sun's brightness, for example. Further, from a succession of photographs secured at short intervals the light-curves of the variables can be readily obtained. The observational material then consists

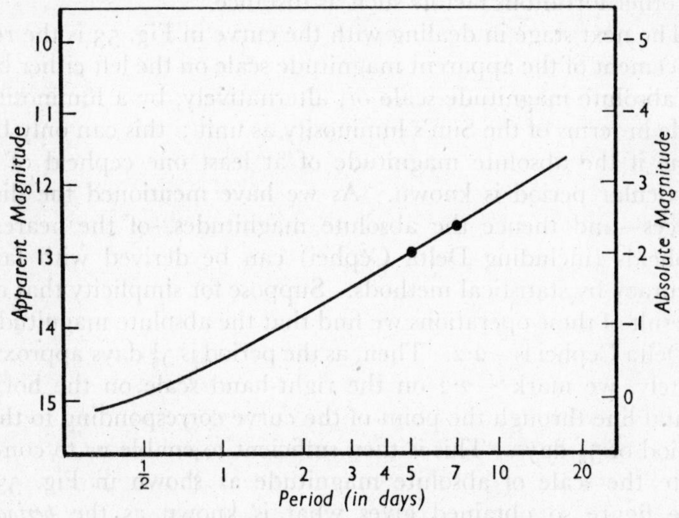

FIG. 53.—Period-Luminosity Relationship

in the case of an individual variable of cepheid type, first, of the period of light-variation and, second, of its average apparent magnitude during the light-cycle. Miss Leavitt noticed that the periods of the brightest stars were the longest, the periods decreasing as the average brightness of the variables diminished, and following this up she succeeded in establishing a general relationship between period and the average brightness of the variables in the Cloud.

This relationship is illustrated in Fig. 53 where the scale of the average apparent magnitude is vertical and the scale relating to period (in days) is horizontal. Investigations of other distant stellar formations produced curves of the same general characteristics although, as might be expected, the numbers attached to the left-hand vertical scale varied according to the formation concerned. It was evident that period was related to luminosity in a very definite way, for it must appear highly improbable that a cepheid with a period of 5 days, say, in one formation should be different intrinsically from a cepheid with exactly the same period in another formation, especially when one realises that cepheid variability is the result of some physical process peculiar to the star itself and independent of all other fortuitous factors such as distance.

The next stage in dealing with the curve in Fig. 53 is the replacement of the apparent magnitude scale on the left either by an absolute magnitude scale or, alternatively, by a luminosity scale in terms of the Sun's luminosity as unit ; this can only be done if the absolute magnitude of at least one cepheid of a particular period is known. As we have mentioned the distances—and thence the absolute magnitudes—of the nearest cepheids (including Delta Cephei) can be derived with fair accuracy by statistical methods. Suppose for simplicity that as a result of these operations we find that the absolute magnitude of Delta Cephei is $-2{\cdot}2$. Then, as the period is $5\frac{1}{3}$ days approximately, we mark $-2{\cdot}2$ on the right-hand scale on the horizontal line through the point of the curve corresponding to the period of $5\frac{1}{3}$ days. This is then sufficient to enable us to complete the scale of absolute magnitude as shown in Fig. 53. The figure so obtained gives what is known as the *period-luminosity relationship*, the foundation of our method whereby we can explore space far beyond the immediate stellar neighbourhood of the Sun.

The importance of the curve is easily demonstrated. Suppose that in a stellar system a cepheid variable is found with a period of, say, 7 days, the period being deduced with comparative ease from a series of photographs, of the same exposure-times, showing the images of the variable as of varying sizes as compared with the images of stars of constant brightness ; further, it is supposed that the average apparent magnitude of the variable during the cycle of light-changes can be determined by one of the usual routine methods. Suppose it is

10·5 ; the curve shows that the absolute magnitude of a cepheid with a period of 7 days is −2·5. It is then a simple calculation to deduce the distance of a star of apparent magnitude 10·5 when its absolute magnitude (that is, the magnitude which the star would have if it were 32½ light-years away) is known to be −2·5.

This is the method used first with great effect by Shapley at the end of the second decade of the present century in deriving the distances of forty globular clusters. The nearest cluster is rather less than 20,000 light-years away and the farthest in which cepheids are found is perhaps 3 or 4 times still farther away.

To measure the distances of the more remote globular clusters in which cepheids were not discernible, Shapley adopted an indirect method. First, considering the 40 clusters with variables, he derived a general correlation between the average absolute magnitude of a score of the brightest stars in a cluster with the average absolute magnitude of its variables. Since the periods of the cluster-variables are less than one day, there is comparatively little variation in the absolute magnitudes of these stars ; accordingly, the average absolute magnitude of the variables remains substantially constant from cluster to cluster. Considering now a score of the brightest stars in such a cluster, Shapley found that the average brightness of these stars was three times the average brightness of the cluster-variables—that is, about 1½ magnitudes brighter. In this way the average absolute magnitude of the score of the brightest stars was obtained. Further, this absolute magnitude was found to be the same, on the whole, for all the 40 clusters containing variables ; there was, then, good ground for the presumption that globular clusters, wherever they may be, were much alike so far as the average absolute magnitude of the score of the brightest stars was concerned. Shapley now turned to a cluster in which variables could not be recognised owing to its remoteness. Routine methods enabled him to derive the average *apparent* magnitude of a score of the brightest stars and, as the corresponding average *absolute* magnitude was now known from the investigation of the 40 clusters containing variables, a step in calculation led him to find the distance of the cluster from us. In this way, Shapley derived reliable distances for most of the clusters outstanding. It will now be shown how this extensive investigation gave us for the first time definite and reasonably precise information about the dimensions of the stellar system of which the Sun is but an inconspicuous member.

On any clear moonless night one of the easily observed features of the sky is the somewhat broad and irregular band of hazy light known as the Milky Way. More than a score of centuries ago it was surmised by the Greek philosopher Democritus that the Milky Way owed its characteristic features to the fact that it was really a vast encircling cloud of stars so numerous and so far away as to be indistinguishable individually. One of the earliest of Galileo's many discoveries was the verification of this ancient speculation. Even with a small telescope the Milky Way is resolved into thousands of stars and with a big telescope literally millions of stars can be seen—or, at any rate, photographed—in an area of the sky not much larger than that covered by the Moon. A remarkably beautiful photograph of part of the Milky Way, in the constellation of Sagittarius, is shown on Plate VI (b) (facing page 129). It was early regarded as more than probable that the stellar system to which we belong was a flattened system much like a thin lens and, even at the beginning of the present century, it was regarded almost as an article of faith that the Sun was situated at or near the centre of the lens. The cloudy effect produced by the Milky Way was then attributed to the great depth to which the stars reached in the principal central plane of the lens ; accordingly the Milky Way—or rather, its plane—must play an important role in the spatial description of the stellar system—or, as we shall refer to it in future, the Galaxy or Galactic System, the words " Galactic " and " Galaxy " being derived from the Greek word for milk. It may be added that stellar systems, wherever they may be, are referred to in general as galaxies.

One of the earliest speculations as to the form or shape of the Galaxy was put forward by Edward Wright of Durham ; he conceived the Galaxy to be of the form of a disc or grindstone with the Sun near the centre—an idea that was later taken up, developed and finally abandoned by Sir William Herschel.

Meanwhile the great nebulae such as that in the constellation of Andromeda (Plate VII, facing page 144) were being studied with the improved telescopes of the time and, towards the end of the eighteenth century, the famous German philosopher Kant expressed the conviction that such nebulae were in fact stellar systems like the Galaxy and well outside the boundaries of the galactic system, an opinion that was not confirmed definitely until midway between the two world wars. Such nebulae as Kant had in mind are now known as extragalactic nebulae.

We now consider Shapley's measurements of the distances of the globular clusters in relation to the Galaxy as a whole and in particular to the plane of the Milky Way or, in briefer nomenclature, the galactic plane. The distances of the clusters in the sky showed that they were disposed in roughly equal numbers on either side of the galactic plane, forming a slightly flattened system ; the inference, fortified by dynamical considerations, seemed to be that the system of clusters was concentric with the Galaxy itself. Now, from a knowledge of the directions and distances of the clusters, the direction and distance of the centre of the cluster-system could be easily ascertained ; the direction proved to be that of the dense stellar clouds in the constellation of Sagittarius where the Milky Way shows a more profuse concentration of stars than anywhere else in its circuit of the heavens. This then must be the direction of the centre of the Galaxy. The distance of the Sun from the centre of the cluster-system and consequently from the galactic centre is now believed to be 30,000 light-years, rather less than that derived in Shapley's original investigations.

The fact that the Sun is at a considerable distance from the centre of the Galaxy can be inferred from the peculiar distribution of the clusters with respect to the Sun (or to ourselves), for nearly all are in one hemisphere of the sky, and not more or less uniformly distributed over the sky as they would be if the Sun had been situated at the centre of the Galaxy. We shall see in Chapter VIII (page 209) that confirmation of these results comes from an unexpected quarter. Meanwhile, by means of Fig. 54, we can give the reader some idea of the large-scale features of the Galaxy and its circumscribing system of clusters. In the figure the small circles represent the globular clusters,

C represents the galactic centre, and S the Sun ; also, the plane through AB perpendicular to the plane of the paper is the galactic plane. The vast majority of the stars lie within the lens-shaped space formed by rotating the full line about DE, although there is no clear-cut boundary. The diameter, AB, of the Galaxy is about 100,000 light-years and its greatest breadth, DE, is perhaps 20 to 30 thousand light-years.

The reader may enquire if it is at all possible to derive some estimate, even if it is rough, of the total number of stars in the Galaxy. We can, of course, count the numbers of stars photographed in sample regions of the sky down to say the 20th

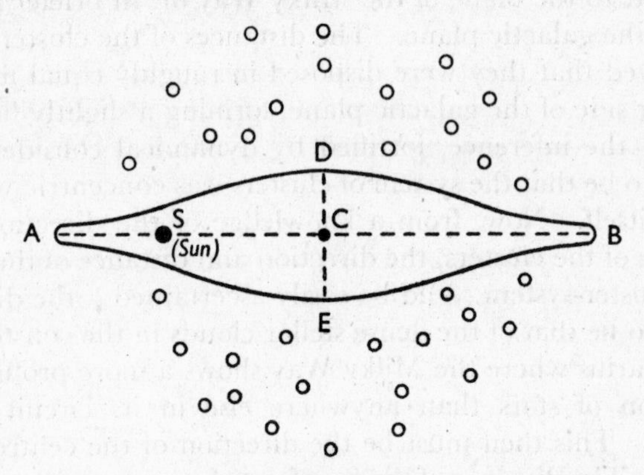

FIG. 54.—Model of Galaxy

magnitude. If the sample regions are regarded as representative, we can then deduce the number of stars in the whole sky as faint as the 20th magnitude. But even with the biggest telescope in the world it is not possible to reach much beyond this limit of magnitude—in other words, we can survey but a portion (and that the nearest) of the Galaxy and certainly very little to the right of DE in Fig. 54. Twenty years ago statistical methods, depending on counts of stars in the different magnitude groups, were employed to furnish the numbers and distribution of the stellar population ; but since then such methods have proved wholly unreliable owing to the discovery that interstellar space is not empty but is in fact populated with atoms, molecules and minute particles which act as a kind of fog, reducing the brightness of the visible stars and effectively screening those at more remote distances.

The method which we alluded to on page 161 as confirming the general dimensions of the Galaxy and which we consider in some detail in the final chapter enables us to make the derived estimate of the numbers of stars in the Galaxy ; the stellar population of the Galaxy is found to be equivalent to a hundred thousand million suns. This result may not carry the degree of accuracy familiar in many astronomical investigations, but it is reasonably certain that the stellar population exceeds one-fifth of the number quoted and is very probably not greater than five times that number. Considering the magnitude and difficulty of the problem, we may regard this result as a very considerable achievement.

The usefulness of cepheids in furnishing distances of formations in which they occur is not limited to the globular clusters. We now make our first substantial excursion outside the bounds of the Galaxy, considering first of all the greater and the lesser Magellanic Clouds. As we have seen, variables of the cepheid type were first discovered by Miss Leavitt in the second of these two objects ; similar variables were also found in the Greater Cloud. From the observed periods of the variables and the period-luminosity relationship the distances of the two clouds are deduced to be 75,000 and 84,000 light-years. The Clouds are comparatively close together in the sky and, as their distances from us are remarkably alike, it follows that their centres must not be more than perhaps 20,000 light-years apart. Recently, long-exposure photographs have revealed immense numbers of fainter stars between the two main Clouds, from which it may be inferred that the Clouds are possibly not two discrete systems but only one, shaped rather like a dumb-bell of which the two main concentrations represent the two Clouds as seen as separate entities by the unaided eye. The Magellanic Clouds are the nearest stellar systems to us, but they are on a distinctly smaller scale than that of the Galaxy.

The discovery of cepheids in the Great Nebula of Andromeda (*v.* Plate VII, facing page 144) enabled E. P. Hubble of Mount Wilson Observatory to determine the distance of this magnificent object, the nearest of the extragalactic nebulae with a spiral structure, by the method with which the reader is now familiar ; it proves to be 700,000 light-years away. From this distance and from measurement of the nebula's extent on photographs, it is easily inferred that its largest diameter is about 60,000 light-years or a little more than half the diameter of the Galaxy. But, as in the case of the Magellanic Clouds, new observational techniques in photographing red stars indicate indisputably that the system is very much larger than was earlier believed and now it would seem that the Great Andromeda Nebula is a galaxy comparable in extent with our galactic system. The recent photographs, referred to, reveal one remarkable feature and that is the disappearance of the spiral characteristics so far as the red stars are concerned. Thus a new complication is introduced into the sufficiently difficult problem of accounting for the spiral structure of such a system, when this particular feature is a property of the white and blue stars and is not shared by the red stars.

Cepheids have been identified in ten extragalactic systems (including the Magellanic Clouds) the most remote of which is about 2 million light-years distant ; it would seem that with the resolving power of the 100-inch telescope at Mount Wilson this is about the maximum distance at which stars of the cepheid type and of luminosities up to about a thousand times that of the Sun can be recognised as individuals in the general mass of the stellar background. No doubt the new 200-inch telescope at Mount Palomar will take us farther afield so far as the detection of cepheids is concerned ; but, meanwhile, other methods must be adopted if we are to throw the fathom line to much greater distances than the investigation of extragalactic cepheids has enabled us to do up to the present. Now one can make particular deductions from the information we have of the neighbouring systems derived by the cepheid method. First, we can compare the total amount of light from a nebula with the light of a third magnitude star, say ; in this way we derive the apparent magnitude of the nebula and a further step, depending on the known distance of the nebula, enables us to calculate its luminosity. It is found that on the average these extragalactic systems are about 40 million times more luminous than the Sun. Second, the average luminosity of, say, twenty of the brightest stars in each of these systems is derived in a similar way ; this average is found to be about 25,000 times the Sun's luminosity.

We have now two criteria for extending our exploration of space. Suppose that we now observe an extragalactic nebula in which the brightest stars are clearly resolved and in which no cepheids have been detected. We can now measure, first, the apparent magnitude of the nebula as a whole and, second, the average magnitude of the twenty brightest stars. If we assume that the external galaxies are very much alike so that the luminosity of any particular one is 40 million times the luminosity of the Sun, we can immediately derive its distance. Similarly, if we assume that the average luminosity of the twenty brightest stars is 25,000 times the luminosity of the Sun we obtain a second estimate of the distance. The distances of about 130 extragalactic systems have been found by the methods described and in the majority of cases the results are satisfactorily accordant ; the most remote of these nebulae is the group of galaxies, the Virgo Cluster, at a distance of about 8 million light-years.

So far, then, it would seem that the underlying hypothesis—that the external galaxies are very much alike—is worthy of considerable confidence. We can now go a stage further and measure the distances of still more remote nebulae in which even the brightest stars cannot be identified as individuals on the photographic plates ; we have now only the first criterion to aid us. By measuring the apparent magnitude of a nebula and assuming that it is, as a whole, 40 million times more luminous than the Sun we can derive its distance.

It is by such means that we have been able to extend our exploration of space to the enormous distance of about 500 million light-years which seems to be the limit attainable by the 100-inch telescope at Mount Wilson. Because of its greatly increased light-gathering power the new 200-inch telescope is expected to detect external galaxies at twice this distance * and, if the sensitivity of photographic plates can be still

* Just after this was written it was announced that preliminary photographs at Mount Palomar revealed objects at a distance of approximately a thousand million light-years.

further increased, this distance will no doubt be greatly exceeded.

One feature of the extragalactic nebulae may be mentioned here and that is the grouping of nebulae in clusters. We have already referred to the cluster in the constellation of Virgo (the Virgin). The ten systems nearest to us—those in which cepheids are detected—appear to form a cluster in which our Galaxy and the Great Nebula in Andromeda are the most prominent members; we may refer to the grouping as the local cluster, the individuals of which lie within a sphere, of diameter roughly one and a half million light-years. One of the most notable clusters is the Coma Cluster—about 50 million light-years distant—in which there are about 500 nebulae congregated within a sphere rather less than two million light-years in diameter. Plate VIII, facing page 145, shows a small group of nebulae in the constellation of Leo.

We turn our attention now to an observational phenomenon of extragalactic nebulae which leads us into strange and unfamiliar regions of thought. On several occasions, previously, we have been concerned with the spectroscopic method of measuring the rate at which a star is receding from us or approaching us. A similar technique is employed in connection with the extragalactic nebulae. When the displacements of the spectral lines are interpreted in terms of velocity-effects the results are surprising. Without exception the nebulae, beyond the confines of the local cluster, appear to be receding from us in much the same way that the individuals of a crowd, in the neighbourhood of an exploding ammunition dump, would scatter with the greatest alacrity so as to put as great a distance as possible between them and the centre of danger. Further, in our analogy, the fastest runners are farthest away from the dump after a minute or two; and so it is with the nebulae, the comparable phenomenon being expressed in the form that the most distant nebulae have the greatest velocities of recession.

It is found, in round figures, that the velocity of recession of nebulae at a distance of one million light-years is on the average about 100 miles per second, at a distance of five million light-years the velocity is 500 miles per second on the average, at a distance of 100 million light-years the velocity is 10,000 miles per second on the average, and so on. The largest recessional velocity so far measured—about 25,000 miles per second—is that of a nebula at a distance of about 250 million light-years. The observational results, a few examples of which we have just given, suggest a definite relationship between recessional velocity and distance which can be expressed statistically in terms of a simple formula, known as the velocity-distance relationship.

It may be asked : Is our interpretation of the displacement of the absorption lines of the nebular spectra in terms of recessional velocity the only one possible ? We add, parenthetically, that there are in the spectra of the distant extragalactic nebulae only a very few lines distinct enough for measurement, the principal ones being the H and K lines of ionised calcium. At various times explanations of the displacements of the spectral lines have been attempted in terms of physical phenomena other than that of velocity, but in all cases these explanations, however plausible at first sight, have suffered shipwreck eventually. We seem then to be forced to accept the only explanation that is consistent throughout, namely, that these immense velocities are real and do actually represent the motions of the nebulae away from us.

We have mentioned the largest recessional velocity so far measured with the 100-inch telescope—it is about one-seventh of the velocity of light ; if, then, the relationship between velocity and distance is accurate, it may be anticipated that the 200-inch telescope will be able to investigate nebulae at very much greater distances whose velocities may be expected to be not far short of one-third of the velocity of light. Moreover, it would be rash to suggest, even although there may be no increase in telescopic power for many years to come, that we have reached a stage at which no further progress—for example, in sensitising photographic plates—can be made ; perhaps, then, in a few years we shall be confronted with recessional velocities one-half, three-quarters or even nine-tenths of the velocity of light. Now, according to the theory of relativity, no velocity can be greater than that of light and, consequently, the nebular velocities must have an upper limit ; and this, in its turn, as a matter of strict argument, must impose a limit to nebular distances unless the velocity-distance relationship proves to be only an approximation, applicable roughly for the distances up to about 250 million light-years so far explored.

In 1915 Einstein published his celebrated theory of relativity; some dozen years later the Einstein universe—as it was called—which conformed to the ideas of the earlier theory, was found to be unstable; there were two alternatives, it must either expand or contract. The discovery of the recessional velocities of the extragalactic nebulae suggested that expansion—and not contraction—of space was taking place; hence, the current doctrine of the "expansion of the Universe", as it is called. It is difficult, or even impossible, to explain the phenomenon in simple terms, for the "space" concerned is not the familiar three-dimensional space of ordinary experience (length, breadth and height), but the four dimensional space, or "continuum", in which time is regarded as a fourth dimension. But perhaps we can give some idea of what is meant in terms of the analogy commonly employed in the present connection.

Suppose we have a large number of minute flies at rest on the surface of a rubber balloon, which is then slowly blown up, its radius increasing at a uniform rate. If we regard the two-dimensional surface of the balloon as the "space" of experience of the flies—we suppose that they can move only on the surface of the balloon—a particular fly A will observe that the distance of any other fly B, measured along the surface of the balloon, is increasing at a constant rate and that the farther B is from A the greater is the velocity of B which would be deduced by A. The flies in fact represent a system of objects any two of which are separating with uniform velocity. It is to be noted that the *surface* of the balloon has no centre, so to speak, and the phenomenon of the expansion of the system of flies would be the common experience of each individual fly.

In somewhat the same way the Universe, like the surface of the balloon, has no centre and the uniform expansion of the Universe involves the separation of the extragalactic nebulae, like the separation of the flies; this, in terms of observation from our Galaxy, is interpreted as the recession of all the other nebulae from us, the observed velocities being proportional to the distances of the particular nebulae from us. The same phenomenon would be observed from the Andromeda Nebula —or from any other. In our analogy, there has been no necessity to postulate any increase in the size of the fly as the balloon is blown up and in the case of the nebulae the " expansion of the Universe " does not involve the expansion of any individual galaxy.

If we accept the doctrine of the expansion, then it follows that in the past the system of the galaxies was less scattered than it is at present. According to Eddington's calculations, the system has doubled its dimensions during the past 1300 million years, and if we go back 3000 million years, or thereby, the galaxies must have been highly concentrated spatially. Can we go back any further or can we say how the expansion began? The Abbé Lemaître, who has been responsible for some significant developments in cosmological theory, has suggested that the expansion was started off with something akin to an explosion, a theory picturesquely described by Mr. F. Hoyle as the " big bang theory ".

However much we may speculate, we must never lose sight of the fact that, before any theory can command general confidence, the sure foundation of accurate observation must first be laid. It is generally agreed that, qualitatively, there can be little doubt about the main features of the recessional velocities of the galaxies, but in some quarters there is less certainty, for example, as to the precise law according to which velocities increase with distance; if this turned out differently from that already referred to, theories would have to be drastically revised. It may not seem surprising, then, that many astronomers elect to adopt a more cautious outlook, believing that theory is at present outstripping observation and preferring to wait until the 200-inch telescope can provide either confirmation of the contemporary trend of thought or, perchance, indisputable evidence of some other phenomenon not envisaged at the present time. Goodricke's discovery of the periodic light-changes of Delta Cephei, with his forecast that the study of variables would probably shed light on the constitution of the stars, has led us into strange regions, undreamed of a third of a century ago.

The aid of Delta Cephei has been invoked in another connection. In the previous chapter we discussed the source of stellar energy and showed how geological evidence, in particular, required that the Earth and the Sun had been in existence for periods greatly in excess of that stipulated by Helmholtz and Kelvin on the basis of the contraction theory. Direct confirmation of the inadequacy of the contraction theory in supplying a star with energy at the requisite rate is provided by Delta Cephei.

The argument is based on a general relation connecting the period of pulsations of a cepheid variable and the average density of the star. On the contraction hypothesis a repetition of Kelvin's calculations, applied now to Delta Cephei, shows that the diameter of a star of the mass and size of Delta Cephei should diminish annually by one part in 40,000 at the present time ; as a consequence, the average density of the star should increase by 3 parts in 40,000. The relation between period and average density then shows that, if Delta Cephei owes the maintainance of its energy-output to gravitational attraction alone, then the period of pulsations must decrease at the present time by about 17 seconds each year. As we have seen, the period of Delta Cephei can be derived with very great accuracy ; as the light-fluctuations of the star have been observed almost continuously over the last hundred years, the verdict should be unequivocal. The diminution of period over the past century is found from observations to be at the rate of approximately one-tenth of a second per annum—a very small fraction of the rate of 17 seconds per annum demanded by the contraction theory. Gravitational contraction can thus supply but one part in 170, approximately, of the energy required to maintain the star's output of heat and light. This conclusion must apply, qualitatively, to the Sun and any other star. It may seem rather remarkable that we have to appeal to a star 600 light-years away to find indisputable proof that we must look beyond gravitational contraction for the source of energy of our luminary.

Chapter VII

EXPLODING STARS

The general subject of this chapter is the class of stars known as " new stars "—or *novae*,* in the established nomenclature ; sometimes these stars are known as " temporary stars ". The names are somewhat misleading, arising as they did before there was any satisfactory knowledge of the phenomena associated with these stars. In pre-telescopic days a nova was a *new* star only in the sense that a bright star had suddenly appeared where no star had previously been seen. Also, the adjective, " temporary " implies, to some extent at least, that a particular and unspecified object has assumed for a short period the status and dignity of a star. As we now know, a nova is and has always been a star, generally so insignificant in the sky as to be undistinguished from myriads of equally faint stars ; all of a sudden something happens and within a few hours the star may rival in brilliance the brightest orb in the heavens ; after a few days, or weeks sometimes, of splendour it fades gradually away, returning eventually to its previous inconspicuous condition, apparently little the worse for its exciting experiences. In the course of its sudden and sometimes spectacular rise to splendour, a typical nova may become perhaps a hundred thousand times more luminous than it was in its undistinguished state ; a change of this magnitude must have been the result of some cataclysmic action of the nature of an internal explosion ; accordingly, such a star may properly be decribed as an *exploding star*.†

Comets and novae have a certain amount in common as regards the unexpectedness of their appearances ; although it is

* A " new star ", in Latin, is *stella nova*—contracted to nova simply ; the plural is novae.

† Some years ago the following appeared (with typical journalistic exaggeration) in the headlines of an American newspaper :

" This news is late, but here it is at last ! Extra !! All about big disasters of 20,000,000 years ago. THREE SUNS BLOWN UP. Information reaches Earth as tiny specks on photographic plates."

true that many comets, beginning with Halley's, have proved to be periodic in character, describing great elongated orbits round the Sun, yet at intervals many comets make their appearance unexpectedly, some of which no doubt will be eventually classed as of the periodic variety when more information about them is gathered. Novae appear without warning ; a few are known to be recurrent, although they do not break out with the regularity associated with the reappearance of the periodic comets. It may be that all novae are liable to explode more than once ; if so, it is certain that the intervals between successive explosions of the very luminous novae are probably of the order of hundreds or even thousands of years.

The earliest nova of which we have definite evidence is the nova of 134 B.C. the appearance of which as we remarked previously (page 10) induced Hipparchus to compile the first catalogue of stellar positions. In 1572 a brilliant nova appeared, so bright that for some weeks it was visible in broad daylight ; this was the star now known as Tycho's nova which the famous Danish astronomer Tycho Brahe asserted, as a result of his observations, to be more remote than the Moon, a conclusion of considerable significance in the contemporary state of astronomy. Tycho's nova is now regarded as a super-nova ; if this is so, Tycho would no doubt have been immensely surprised if he had been told that his star was about two hundred thousand million times farther off than the Moon ! We have remarked that after their outbursts novae return to their previous states of insignificance ; we add that the pre-nova states (when known) and the post-nova states are characterised by certain peculiarities, but despite this knowledge the efforts to locate Tycho's star have so far proved fruitless.

The next nova appeared in 1604 and at its brightest was no whit inferior to Jupiter, outshining the brightest stars in the sky. It was visible to the naked eye from October 1604 to March 1606, but as the telescope had not been invented its subsequent history could not be followed. This nova, now known as Kepler's nova, was responsible for the first published investigation of Galileo who succeeded in demonstrating that the star was farther off than the planets—a modest step in the right direction as compared with Tycho's conclusion ! A tiny patch of nebulosity near the position assigned by Kepler is now assumed to be associated with the now-defunct nova.

Before passing on to the much more informative novae of recent years we refer to the less well authenticated nova of 1054 A.D., the appearance of which is reported in Chinese writings and confirmed in Japanese records. There is no indication as to its apparent brightness at maximum but presumably the star attained such outstanding brilliance as, first, to be easily detected and, second, to have been deemed worthy of specific mention. There are very definite reasons for believing that the *Crab Nebula* (see Plate IX, facing page 176) is intimately associated with the nova and as the distance of the former is known to be about 4000 light-years we can make a guess as to the nova's brightness at maximum.

Assume first that the nova was of the normal variety, as opposed to the class of super-novae already referred to ; then from our present knowledge of novae in general it would seem that at brightest the nova must have been of the fourth magnitude, or thereabouts, and probably not sufficiently remarkable to excite notice in the records of the time. But if the new star were of the category of super-novae, its brightness at maximum must have been about twenty times that of Sirius and half a dozen times brighter even than Tycho's nova ; surely such a star would be worthy of record. Yet in the admittedly scanty European literature of the time there is not the slightest allusion to such an extraordinary celestial phenomenon ; despite this absence of supporting evidence it is generally agreed that the new star was a super-nova.

For nearly three centuries after the appearance of Kepler's nova (in 1604), such novae as were detected in the galactic system were comparatively inconspicuous even at maximum brightness. In 1901 a new star appeared in the constellation of Perseus which reached the first magnitude, and in 1918 a still brighter nova appeared in the constellation of Aquila. We remark in parenthesis that novae are generally referred to by the constellation in which they appear and by the year of the visible outburst ; thus the two novae to which we have alluded are known respectively as Nova Persei (1901) and Nova Aquilae (1918). In both instances the parts of the sky in which they appeared had been photographed a few days before their outbursts and consequently the magnitudes previous to the nova-stage were readily obtained. We shall describe in some detail the light-changes of Nova Persei (1901) illustrated in the light-curve (Fig. 55), although some features cannot be represented accurately in the figure.

The nova was discovered on 21st February by a keen amateur astronomer T. D. Anderson, of Edinburgh ; it was then a star of the third magnitude. Two days before discovery the region

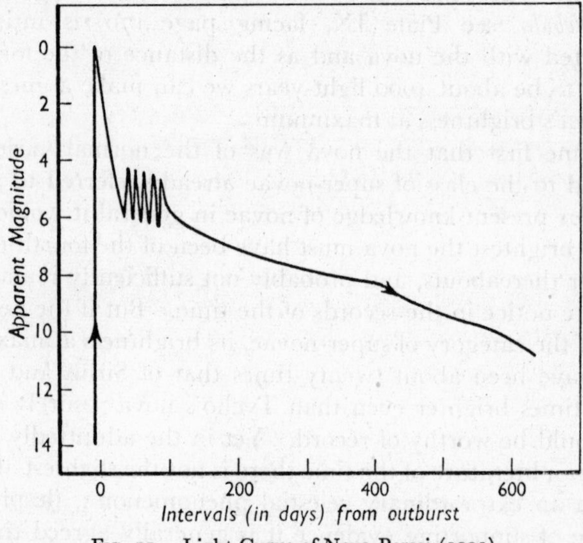

FIG. 55.—Light-Curve of Nova Persei (1901)

of the sky in which the nova appeared had been photographed at Harvard Observatory and the star was then of the 13th magnitude. At the time of discovery the nova was about 10,000 times more luminous than it was two days previously. A vast increase in luminosity such as this must be the consequence of an immense increase in the size of the star or in the surface temperature or in both. There is little doubt—as the later evidence will indicate—that the main factor contributing to the immense increase in a nova's luminosity is the expansion of the star. Returning to observations of Nova Persei (1901) we find that two days after discovery the star attained its maximum brightness, being then as bright as Capella and Vega—two of the chief orbs in the northern sky. At this point in the light-curve the star had become nearly 200,000 times more luminous than in its pre-nova condition. If we disregard changes of surface-temperature during the rise to maximum we must conclude that the star's radius had increased 450-fold. As we now know the distance of the star with fair accuracy, we can easily infer that Nova Persei (1901) began its spectacular career as a dwarf star, probably much smaller than the Sun, attaining at maximum the splendour of a super-giant.

Almost immediately after it had reached maximum brightness, the nova began to fade away ; within a week it was of the second magnitude and, two weeks later, of the fourth magnitude. Then for some weeks a series of oscillations set in—a feature peculiar to this star and, in a minor degree, to Nova Aquilae (1918)—of period four days approximately and of a range of nearly two magnitudes ; thus, during the interval of oscillation the star might be easily visible as a star of approximately the fourth magnitude and two days later it would be at or slightly beyond the limit of vision at the sixth magnitude, brightening up in about two more days to near the fourth magnitude. Sir Robert Ball, then Director of the University Observatory at Cambridge, was wont to recount humorously his experiences during this phase of the star's variability ; one night he went out on his lawn to show some visitors the new star but it had disappeared from view ; two nights later he invited other friends " to observe the star that had disappeared " but, when they looked, there it was " as large as life ". Two nights later other visitors were invited to see the star that had, apparently, come to life again so miraculously ; but it had disappeared once more ! After several weeks of such oscillations the star continued on its downward path of luminosity, reaching roughly its pre-nova magnitude about 30 years after its outburst.

The star continues to be carefully scrutinised and Dr. W. H. Steavenson and Mr. B. M. Peek, who faithfully keep watch on it, report each year that there are still unmistakable fluctuations in brightness. It may be added that pre-nova observations of the star, such as they were, indicated that the star was not of fixed brightness.

It is not to be supposed that the light-curves of all novae resemble that in Fig. 55 with an immediate and rapid decline in brightness within one or two days of reaching maximum. Nova Herculis (1934) may be cited as an example of a nova which appeared to be disinclined to shed its glory. Discovered on 13th December by Mr. J. P. M. Prentice, an ardent observer of meteors, it was zealously observed at Cambridge; after several nights of exacting spectroscopic observations, the observers reckoned that, if the nova behaved like most of the previous novae which diminished in brightness soon after maximum, it would be too faint for observation just before the Christmas vacation. The star, however, stubbornly refused to depart substantially from its maximum brightness; observing enthusiasm and a spell of excellent nights combined to provide a mass of spectroscopic observational material unusual in the case of novae. One week succeeded another and still the nova remained sufficiently bright for observational purposes; the Easter season was approaching and surely the star would be considerate enough to give the weary observers a well-deserved rest; but no, it continued within the range of the instruments for some further weeks. As might be expected this exacting series of observations furnished a mine of information about the changing phenomena exhibited by the nova.

Until a score or two of years ago the discovery of a nova was entirely fortuitous, although it must be added that the discoverer was invariably someone completely familiar with the constellations. One nova—Nova Geminorum (1903)—was discovered in a rather peculiar way at Oxford University Observatory while a plate for the astrographic catalogue was being secured. It should be mentioned as a preliminary that during a photographic exposure the telescope must be mechanically driven at precisely the rate at which the stars move across the heavens as a result of the rotation of the Earth about its axis; for this purpose a small telescope called a "finder" with perpendicular cross-wires in the focal plane of the eye-piece is mounted on the tube of the principal telescope; the setting is made so that a rather bright star defines the centre of the region of the sky to be photographed and the instrument is adjusted so that this star (known as the guiding-star) is seen exactly at the

IX. Crab Nebula
(Mt. Wilson Observatory)

X(a). The Pleiades Nebulosity (*I. Roberts*)

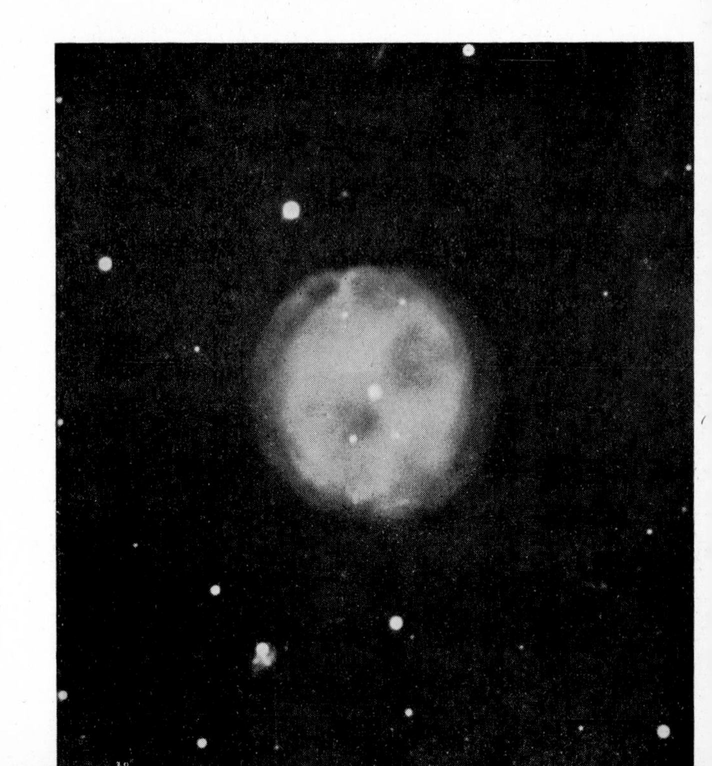

X(b). Owl Nebula
(*Mt. Wilson Observatory*)

intersection O of the crosswires in the finder. If we ignore the effect of refraction, the star will remain at O during the exposure provided that the mechanical apparatus is performing its function with complete accuracy. If the " driving " is not accurate, the star is seen to drift slightly away from O ; when this occurs the observer, by means of subsidiary controls, alters the adjustment of the instrument so as to bring back the star to O. On the occasion concerned the observer, swinging the telescope approximately into the position required and looking through the finder, picked out what he thought was the particular guiding-star and then made the exposures in the usual way. When the plate was developed it was seen that the region photographed was not quite that corresponding to the intention of the observer. On investigation it was immediately found that the guiding-star employed was a nova actually on the upward rise, and news of the discovery was soon flashed to all observatories interested in " new " stars.

In recent times Harvard Observatory, for example, has undertaken the systematic photography of the heavens, at frequent intervals, with instruments covering a large area of the sky at a single exposure ; one object of this routine work is the detection of novae so that the great telescopes may be turned on these stars without delay and perchance obtain spectroscopic records when the novae are still increasing in brightness—a part of the life-history of these stars for which spectroscopic information is singularly deficient.

Almost without exception the novae appearing in our galactic system are found in Milky Way regions where the stellar population is of course at its densest. Although really bright novae are seen only at comparatively long intervals it is estimated that, on the average, about two dozen novae as bright as, or brighter than, the ninth magnitude at maximum appear in the galactic system annually. This is probably an underestimate since the dense star clouds of the Milky Way will render the detection of a nova, considerably brighter than the ninth magnitude, a matter of the utmost difficulty and improbability. But taking the figure as reasonably accurate and assuming that the number of stars in the Galaxy is a hundred thousand million, it would then appear that, on an average a star can become a nova once in about four thousand million years—a period of time that is close to the age assigned to the stars of the Galaxy. At first sight it might seem that every star is capable of going through a nova-phase ; but later we shall see that there is evidence that several novae are recurrent and further that novae in general belong to a definitely restricted type of star.

We consider briefly one or two salient features relating to the spectra of novae, for it would be impossible within the compass of a few pages to describe and interpret the numerous and complex changes that occur almost daily in the spectra of any particular nova. Nor do all novae produce identical spectra, although the principal features are common to all. As there seems to be little doubt about the main sequence of events in the outburst and subsequent career of a nova it will be convenient to deal with the interpretation of the spectral phenomena step by step on the basis, first, that the immense increase in the luminosity of the star is the consequence primarily of the rapid expansion of the star and, second, that at or near maximum one or more shells of stellar matter are thrown off with immense speeds.

It should be remarked, however, that we are wholly ignorant, observationally, of the phenomena occurring immediately after the outburst has started. This is hardly surprising since most of the recent novae have been stars of the tenth to the fifteenth apparent magnitude ; the most that one can hope for is that the discovery of a future nova will take place not later than the time that the star has reached about halfway on its rise to maximum. It would be too optimistic to expect that a really near star, such as one of the components of 61 Cygni (of apparent magnitude about $5\frac{1}{2}$) would oblige contemporary astronomers by turning into a nova with the range in brightness characteristic of the average galactic nova ; in such an event discovery would almost certainly follow closely on the outburst of the star and our instruments would have the unique opportunity of recording the attendant phenomena through a very large part of the upward rise in the brightness to maximum, when the star might be a hundred times brighter than Sirius.

Up to the time of maximum light the spectrum consists of

absorption lines of such gases as hydrogen, nitrogen and oxygen, and of such metals as iron, titanium and ionised calcium and magnesium, on a background of continuous spectrum, the whole indicating a star of great luminosity. These absorption lines are displaced towards the violet end of the spectrum and from the measurements of the displacements the rate of expansion of the star's atmosphere—of the order of several hundred miles per second—is derived. In the case of Nova Aquilae (1918) the star before the outburst was known to be of spectral type A and there was little or no change in this respect through the observed range up to the time of maximum ; as the relative constancy of spectral type indicates little change in surface-temperature, it follows that the increase in brightness must be attributed, almost entirely, to increase in the star's surface-area, that is, to the expansion of the star.

It would seem then that we are on safe ground in believing that the immense increase in brightness of novae in general is related substantially to the rapid expansion of the stars, of the order of magnitude which we found (page 175) for Nova Persei (1901). This conclusion is reinforced when we compare the pre-maximum spectra of novae which rise rapidly to maximum and of others which increase in brightness at a more leisurely rate ; in the spectra of the former the velocities indicated by displacements of the absorption lines are generally much greater than the velocities inferred from the spectra of the latter ; the relation, then, between a "fast" nova and a "slow" nova is a matter of the relative rates of expansion of the two stars.

The next stage occurs at or near maximum when broad bright lines (or bands) appear on the redward side of the absorption lines ; this phenomenon, together with the fact that the nova begins to fade in brightness, is interpreted in terms of the gradual contraction of the main body of the star and the continued expansion of its outer gaseous layers, thus giving rise to the expanding shell previously alluded to.

The situation shortly after the separation of the shell from the star is indicated in Fig. 56 in which, for simplicity, we assume that the expanding shell is moving outwards symmetrically with respect to the star. Now the combination of the continuous spectrum—arising from the photospheric regions of the collapsing star—and the absorption lines must mean that the absorbing atoms are directly between us and the star ; the atoms which are distinctively marked at A (within the cylindrical beam of light between the star and the Earth) are then responsible for the observed absorption lines ; the measured velocity of approach derived from these lines is interpreted as the rate of expansion of the shell—we can ignore, in this connection, the presumably very much smaller velocity of approach or of recession, of the star itself. Consider now the part of the shell other than that at A ; as we shall see later, the atoms of

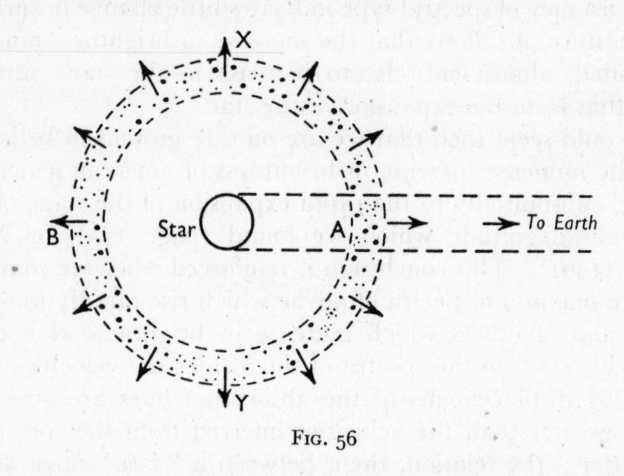

FIG. 56

several elements in the shell are induced by the powerful radiation of the star to emit light in certain wave-lengths.

The atoms referred to are moving radially outwards from the star ; those on the Earth-ward side of the star have radial velocities of approach varying from zero at X and Y (where the outward motion is at right angles to the line of sight) to the approach velocity derived from the outward motions of the atoms at A ; such atoms will then give a broad bright line on the red-ward side of the corresponding absorption line. In the same way the atoms of the shell on the opposite side of the star from the Earth will give a succession of bright lines (merging in a broad bright line) whose displacements are still farther towards the red end of the spectrum since now the radial velocities concerned are velocities of recession. The total effect is then that the absorption line is bordered on its red-ward side by a broad bright line or band, double the width of each of the two bright lines referred to, the centre of which corresponds to zero radial velocities of the atoms at X and Y.

Later, the absorption lines fade and the bright lines arising from the metallic atoms gradually disappear. The interpretation at this stage is that the expansion of the shell has proceeded to such an extent that the density of the material has been greatly reduced resulting, first, in the diminution in the number of the absorbing atoms and, second, in producing the conditions in which metallic atoms are readily ionised by the still powerful ultra-violet radiation from the star, any radiation now produced by such atoms being outside the range of the observable spectrum.

Later still, the so-called nebulium lines become prominent, the principal of which is a pair of green lines arising from the peculiar radiations of the oxygen atom which has lost two electrons. Many years ago it was supposed that such lines, observed in several nebulae, must be attributed to a hitherto unknown element to which the name " nebulium " was given ; but recently Dr. I. S. Bowen, now Director of the Mount Wilson Observatory, gave a convincing demonstration that such lines are produced by ionised oxygen and nitrogen atoms existing in conditions of density—about a billionth that of ordinary air —far remote from the most perfect " vacuum " that can be produced by mechanical means in our laboratories. The presence of the nebulium lines in the spectrum makes quite definite the fact that at this stage of its expansion the density of the outward-moving shell has become incredibly minute. As the expansion progresses and the star continues to fade, the bright lines gradually disappear leaving the rather feeble continuous spectrum of the star behind ; eventually, the star reaches the stage of insignificance at, or near, which the outburst began and the shell becomes still more tenuous, being finally dissipated into regions of space far distant from the parent star. We shall refer later to the expanding shell in another connection.

In the preceeding summary we have based our arguments on a single shell expanding uniformly and symmetrically with respect to the star. In some instances the phenomena are more complex. For example, the absorption lines in the earlier stages are sometimes doubled and even tripled, suggesting that two or more shells are thrown off at different times with different speeds.

Again, the expanding shell is not always symmetrical as it is in the case of Nova Aquilae (1918), the suggestion in this particular instance being that the initial disturbance or explosion is so deep-seated that it affects all parts of the surface-layers with more or less equal intensity.

The evidence comes from observational material different from that we have just been considering, namely, the spectroscopic phenomena. There comes a point at which the star

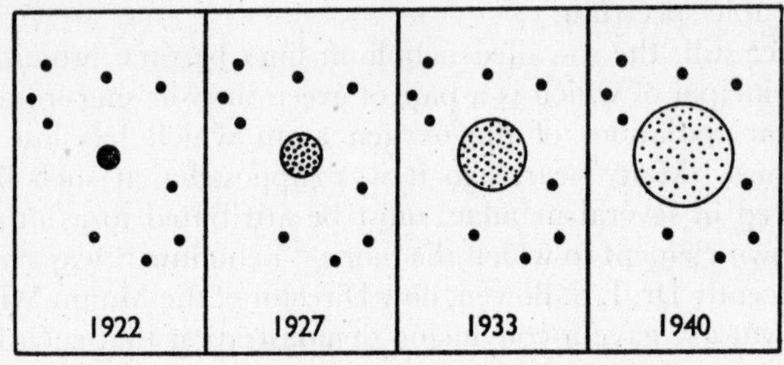

FIG. 57.—Expanding Shell of Nova Aquilae (1918)

and its shell become so faint that it is no longer possible to record a spectrum owing to instrumental limitations. But before this stage is reached direct photographs of long exposure confirm the existence of a shell and the fact that the shell is expanding. For example, a few months after maximum a minute disc was seen around Nova Aquilae (1918) which, gradually expanding, was comparable in size, about a year and a half after maximum, with the disc of the planet Neptune. Year by year the disc increased in angular diameter at a substantially uniform rate—about 2 seconds of arc per annum—until 1941 when its greatly increased faintness made further observations of this kind impossible. These changes are illustrated in Fig. 57, based on Mount Wilson photographs.

On the other hand, the " shell " associated with Nova Persei

(1901)—if we may use this term—and discovered only in 1917 is anything but symmetrical, being roughly semi-circular in form just as if the initial disturbance or explosion had occurred about halfway, say, between the star's centre and surface ; in this event, it might be expected that only one hemisphere of the star would be markedly affected.

We have already mentioned the Crab Nebula in connection with novae ; it is found from long exposure photographs that the nebula is expanding in much the same way as the shell around Nova Aquilae (1918). The known angular dimensions of the nebula and the angular rate (assumed uniform) at which it is expanding suggest that the expansion started about 900 years ago A.D., and the reasonable inference follows that the nova of 1054 A.D., mentioned in Chinese and Japanese records to which we have previously referred, is the progenitor of the Crab Nebula (see Plate IX, facing page 176).

We mention two other nebulae with unsymmetrical expansions. About three years after the discovery of Nova Pictoris (1925) the nova appeared to be surrounded by a nebulous disc about a second of arc in diameter. Some little time later the startling announcement was made that the object had developed into a close double star. It is not known definitely how double-stars—or more accurately, binary stars—come into being ; one explanation is in terms of fission, the division of a rapidly rotating star into two components. Was Nova Pictoris supplying ocular evidence of the soundness of the theory? Subsequent observations complicated the matter still more when the object appeared to be a triple formation, with the occasional suspicion that a fourth component was present. Soon, however, it was seen that the two original " components " were separating and it was realised that the triple system consisted of two nebulous " knots " or fragments of shell between which the star itself was visible. Unfortunately the telescopic equipment in the southern hemisphere at the time was of insufficient power to prolong observations of this interesting nova beyond 1931.

The history of Nova Herculis (1934) is similar to that just recounted. About seven months after discovery the nova seemed to be like a close double star, but subsequent observations showed that these individual knots were separating, the true star appearing between them later. In 1940 the knots disappeared as prominent features, being replaced by a nebulous disc of elliptical shape which, two years later, was transformed by expansion into a nebulous ring surrounding the star. Three other nebulae, Nova Aurigae (1891), Nova Cygni (1920), and Nova Lacertae (1935), show expanding nebulosity.

So far we have made no reference to the distances of the novae and we now deal with this important matter since the knowledge of the distance of a particular nova enables us to calculate its luminosity (in terms of the Sun's luminosity as unit)—or, alternatively, its absolute magnitude—at all stages of its career when we have the relevant information. We have remarked in a previous chapter that the fundamental method of measuring a star's distance—the surveyor's method—is ineffective if the distance exceeds four or five hundred light-years. The distances of the well-observed novae all exceed this limiting distance and it is hardly surprising that the fundamental method has proved unsuccessful in giving reliable information. Indirect methods must then be looked for.

An ingenious method was suggested by Kapteyn in connection with Nova Persei (1901). A few months after maximum the star seemed to be immersed in, or adjacent to, a rapidly expanding nebula ; the rate of expansion appeared to be so enormous that it was soon realised that the movement of actual material was out of the question. Kapteyn made the suggestion that the phenomenon was simply the progressive illumination of a dark nebula near the nova as the waves of light of the outburst travelled outwards to ever-increasing distances from the star. Suppose, for example, that the star is situated within an enormous dark nebula and that the rate at which it is illuminated by the outward travelling light of the outburst is one degree per annum * ; the distance travelled in one year by the light is of course one light-year, and we then have the simple problem to calculate the distance of the nova such that a distance of one light-year subtends an angle of one degree at the Earth ; the answer in this particular instance is 57 light-years. In the actual case of Nova Persei the nebula was mainly

* The observed rate was about one-third of this.

on one side of the star and in the absence of information as to its exact situation the deduced distance of about 300 light-years was open to serious doubt. It should be added that the nebula with which we have just been concerned must not be confused with the expanding shell, observed later as nebulosity, thrown off from the star itself.

The principle of the preceeding method can be applied to certain novae for which we have the requisite information. Consider Nova Aquilae (1918) and its symmetrical expanding shell. The radial velocity derived from the absorption lines in the spectrum indicates a velocity of expansion of about 1000 miles per second or roughly a two-hundredth part of a light-year per annum. Direct photographs show that the angular radius of the nebulosity is expanding at the rate of about one second of arc per annum. The calculation of the distance of the nova follows easily as in the previous case ; the result is about 1000 light-years ; with more accurate data than we have used here the distance of the nebula has been variously given as about 1200 light-years or about 1400 light-years.

The distances of seven galactic novae have been found in this way ; the nearest is Nova Herculis (1934) at a distance of about 750 light-years and the most distant is Nova Cygni (1920) which is nearly 5000 light-years away ; by this method the distance of Nova Persei (1901) is given as about 1550 light-years. It may be remarked that the greatest linear velocity of a shell thrown out by a nova is about 2400 miles per second in the case of Nova Lacertae (1936). In the same way the distance of the Crab Nebula has been calculated to be 4000 light-years ; the observed linear rate of expansion is about 800 miles per second.

The information derived from the distances of the individual galactic novae so far investigated is, no doubt, not so exact as we should wish, but nevertheless we seem to be on surer grounds when we consider the novae as a group ; in other words we hope by taking an average to smooth out the observational uncertainties. We find, in this way, that the average absolute magnitude at maximum of the novae concerned is somewhere in the region of $-6{\cdot}5$ so that these stars at their brightest are about 30,000 times more luminous than the Sun, rivalling—in some cases surpassing—the luminosities of the super-giants of the galactic system.

Having established the absolute magnitude at maximum, we can go a stage farther and derive the absolute magnitude of the average nova before the outburst occurs. As we have remarked previously, some of the earlier novae of the present century can be identified with faint stars which appear on photographic plates taken, in some instances, for purposes unconnected with the detection of novae. In recent years the " patrol " of the heavens at Harvard Observatory, for example, will ensure a knowledge of the condition of a future bright nova antecedent to its outburst. Meanwhile, it is known that the range of magnitude between the pre-nova stage and maximum brightness of the principal novae of recent times is 11 to 13 magnitudes, the former corresponding to an increase of luminosity by a factor of 25,000 and the latter by a factor of about 150,000. The circumstances of the particular novae concerned indicate that before outburst they are dwarf stars with absolute magnitudes very close to the range of $+6$ to $+7$, that is, stars with luminosities from about one-third to one-fifth of the luminosity of the Sun.

It is also known in one or two instances that before outburst the stars were bluish in colour, indicating a temperature very much higher than that of the Sun ; if this applies in general to the bright novae we have been considering it seems reasonably certain that the radius of the pre-nova star can be little different, in round figures, from 50,000 miles—not much greater than one-tenth of the radius of the Sun. Such stars are evidently closely related to the white-dwarfs we discussed in Chapter III. The available evidence suggests that, after outburst, novae return to or near the luminosity of pre-nova days ; further, the surface-temperatures are of the order of 40,000° C., corresponding to spectral type O.

We come now to the interesting class of novae which have exploded on more than one occasion. There are three well-authenticated members of the group, the years in which the outbursts occurred being indicated ; (i) Nova Ophiuchi (1898 and 1933), (ii) Nova Pyxidis (1890, 1902 and 1920) and (iii) Nova Scorpii (1863, 1906 and 1936). Of these the brightest is Nova Ophiuchi which rose from about the twelfth magnitude to about the fourth, the range in magnitude being $7\frac{1}{2}$ magnitudes. It is noteworthy that the light-curves on the two occasions of its outbursts are practically identical. In the case of the bright novae with which we were concerned earlier, the fading from maximum to the pre-nova magnitude is a slow business requiring on the average from 20 to 30 years ; in the case of Nova Ophiuchi the fading after the outburst of 1933 was much more rapid, only three years being spent in this phase.

The second recurrent nova, Nova Pyxidis, has much the same range of magnitude as the first, rising from the fourteenth magnitude to nearly the sixth. The third, Nova Scorpii, reached the ninth magnitude at maximum and although the range is not known very accurately, it is probably little different from that of the other two novae ; also, the light-curves on the occasion of two of its outbursts are almost identical.

We consider at this stage a class of variable stars known as the U Geminorum stars, or sometimes the SS Cygni stars, so called after the best known members of the class. These are stars with nova-like light-curves, characterised by a very rapid rise to maximum but with a much more rapid decline in brightness relatively than is found in the case of the bright novae. The average periods between outbursts vary for the group from about 10 days to 10 months. The intervals between successive maxima of a particular star are anything but constant ; for example, the intervals between successive maxima of U Geminorum vary approximately between 60 and 260 days. It is noteworthy that the ranges in magnitude between the normal states of the stars and maximum brightness appear to be correlated, qualitatively at least, with the average intervals between successive maxima which we may describe as average periods. Thus, for stars with average periods of 15 days, the range in brightness is 3 magnitudes approximately ; for average periods of 60 days, the range is 4 magnitudes ; and for average periods of 200 days, the range is 5 magnitudes. When it is remembered that the periods of an individual star such as U Geminorum fluctuate over a wide range it is perhaps inadvisable to push this correlation beyond reasonable bounds ; nevertheless it may not be too rash to suggest that the U

Geminorum stars are functionally related to the recurrent novae.

Can we go a stage further and connect up the U Geminorum stars, the recurrent novae and the bright galactic novae ? If there is some relation between " period " and range of magnitude, then it might be expected that the bright novae would have outbursts at intervals, very approximately, of a thousand years. In some departments of observational astronomy progress must await the passage of time, as is notably the case in the observations of binary stars and in the observations for deriving the proper motions of distant objects, although in such instances much can be learned even within the life-time of any astronomer. But the recurrence of the nova-phenomena in such stars as Nova Persei (1901) can only be a subject of speculation at present—with, perhaps in later centuries, some supporting evidence derived from other considerations—but probably not verifiable observationally for a span of time surpassing the whole extent, to date, of the Christian era.

The possibility that the Sun may become a nova in the immediate future can be judged on what we know of the phenomena characteristic of novae in their pre-outburst state. First, the evidence seems to suggest quite firmly that the bright novae were initially hot stars with white dwarf characteristics. Second, such information as we have indicates that in the pre-nova stage the stars concerned are not constant in brightness, with variations of one magnitude at least. On both grounds it seems reasonably reassuring to affirm that the Sun is, at present, not of the type of stars of which the bright novae are made. Nor is it obviously of the type of the recurrent novae with periods of a score or so of years nor of the U Geminorum stars with periods measured in days. The Sun is, of course, a slightly variable star—the presence of sun-spots in varying numbers and extent and the minor eruptions of the proninences bear witness to this statement—but the degree of variability is infinitesimal compared with the pre-nova variability referred to ; in fact, if the Sun's luminosity increased by a factor equivalent to the change of a single magnitude it is certain that the death-knell of all forms of life on the Earth would be sounded.

Although the present stability of the Sun is, then, not in question on the above grounds, there remains the unsolved problem of the origin of white dwarfs or of stars closely related to them. The proportion of white dwarfs in the stellar population within a few score of light-years of the Sun is considerable ; to some, this suggests that normal stars may suddenly collapse, through evolutionary processes, into bodies which may eventually flare up into novae ; to others, it seems more reasonable to suggest that white dwarfs are the relics of the nova phenomena. We do not know the answer to the riddle, but on the other hand there is not the slightest shred of evidence that the Sun will depart from its present state of stability for many aeons to come.

So far we have been discussing novae that have appeared in our Galactic system—over 80 have been observed to date. As we are immersed in a welter of stars we are handicapped in noticing what is happening beyond a distance of about 5000 light-years in the Galaxy. This disadvantage disappears when we turn our telescopes on the nearest of the extragalactic systems. Well over a hundred novae have been detected in the Great Nebula of Andromeda alone (Plate VII, facing page 144) and a relatively large number in other extragalactic systems including the Great and the Lesser Magellanic Clouds. It is noteworthy that only one nova has been seen in the direction of a globular cluster ; but competent authorities are of the opinion that this particular star is not actually associated with the cluster, being simply a galactic nova seen projected against the background of the cluster stars.

In recent years the Andromeda nebula has been kept under almost continuous observation at Mount Wilson Observatory and we are indebted to Dr. E. P. Hubble for a wealth of information relating to the novae appearing in this system. We have seen in the previous chapter that the distance of the system is known with a high degree of accuracy ; with this information and the observed apparent magnitude at maximum of a particular nova, the absolute magnitude at maximum can be easily deduced. If we omit, for the moment, the famous super-nova of 1885, the Andromeda novae prove, on the average, to be stars of absolute magnitude—5·5 at maximum, that is to say, about one-half to one-third of the average luminosity of the bright galactic novae. It is not known that this comparatively small discrepancy is real ; it can arise as a result of under-estimating somewhat the distance of the system or of over-estimating the distances of the comparatively few galactic novae for which there is adequate information or of including in the Andromeda statistics those novae with possible ranges, between minimum and maximum, rather less than the range of 11 or 13 magnitudes appertaining to the galactic novae concerned. In connection with the latter alternative it should be noticed that at maximum the Andromeda novae are no brighter than the sixteenth apparent magnitude and that their brightness in the pre-nova stage—and consequently, too, the range through which they brighten—is not known. The novae in the Magellanic Clouds are found to be of practically the same luminosity at maximum as the average nova in the Andromeda nebula.

The class of super-novae is best represented by the gigantic stellar outburst in the Andromeda nebula already alluded to. It was first seen on 17th August, 1885, and by the end of the month it had reached to nearly the sixth apparent magnitude, a brilliant object near the heart of the great nebula. There was no sign of the super-nova a day previous to its discovery and a photograph taken just a year before, showing stars as bright as the fifteenth magnitude, demonstrated beyond any shadow of doubt that the star, at the time, was fainter than the magnitude just mentioned. After maximum the star's light faded quickly and by March of the following year the star had passed beyond the reach of the largest telescopes. There can be very little doubt that the star actually belongs to the extra-galactic system and is not a foreground star. At the time of the outburst astronomical spectroscopy was still in its infancy, but the available evidence is conclusive that the spectrum of the super-nova was similar to the spectra of the galactic novae at or near maximum.

The outburst of a typical nova in our system pales almost into insignificance as compared with the outburst of the super-nova. At maximum, the star's absolute magnitude was close to -14 or -15 and its luminosity then is thus not far short of 10,000 times the luminosity of a nova such as Nova Persei (1901) and a hundred million times greater than the Sun. The super-nova in Andromeda is not the only member of its class, for nearly two score of similar stars in several extragalactic systems have been observed recently at Mount Wilson and elsewhere. It is believed, as stated earlier, that the Crab Nebula is associated with a super-nova (1054 A.D.) and likewise Tycho's Nova of 1572 is generally assigned to this class of exploding stars.

We return to further consideration of that characteristic feature of such novae as Nova Aquilae (1918), namely, the expanding shell visible some months (or longer) after the actual outburst. The appearance of the shell invites comparison with a class of celestial object known as a "planetary nebula" about 150 of which are known in the galactic system; a well-known example is the "Owl Nebula" shown in Plate X (b) (facing page 177). These objects are at very great distances from us—the nearest is estimated to be about 3000 light-years away and the farthest perhaps as far off as the centre of the galaxy. The small number of the known planetaries and their great distances combine to make it certain that these bodies are extremely rare in the galactic system—a point of some importance in discussing the possible relation of planetaries and novae.

The central star of such an object as the "Owl Nebula" is one of the hottest objects in the heavens, the surface-temperature being of the order of 50,000° C. with which is associated the intensely blue colour of the star. Such a star's radiation is mainly in the ultra-violet region of the spectrum and it is this intense radiation which is responsible for the characteristic features of the light emitted from the surrounding shell. The spectrum of the shell shows the bright nebulium lines which, as we have stated, appear in the later stages of a nova's career arising from the expanding shell; in both cases the matter of which the respective shells are constituted must be of almost incredible tenuity. There is thus a very definite similarity between the two types of objects; further, it must be added, the central star of the typical planetary and the nova long after its outburst are very much alike in physical characteristics.

Despite these similarities the balance of opinion appears to be strongly against the suggestion that planetary nebulae are former novae. In the first place, the appearance of a nova is far from being an isolated phenomenon in the heavens and, consequently, we should expect to find a considerably greater number of planetaries within a distance of, say, 5000 light-years than the telescope reveals if the two types of objects were intimately related. Second, a planetary nebula appears to be a relatively stable structure ; in several cases, the planetary shell is found to be expanding very slowly, the greatest rate of expansion being no more than about 35 miles per second which is almost negligible compared with the rates of expansion, of the order of a thousand miles per second, of the shells of many of the novae. Third, over the years during which the planetaries have been observed there is little evidence that the planetary envelope has altered in any conspicuous way, suggesting that the planetary nebula has elements of permanence ; the expanding shells of the novae, on the other hand are transient features being observable over a period of perhaps a score of years, after which the material of the fast-expanding shell is dissipated into interstellar space.

What is the explanation of a nova outburst ? Half a century ago, or less, it was supposed that a couple of stars collided or, at least, came within close range of one another, with catastrophic results. This speculation can now be ruled out, for within recent years we have learned a great deal about the numbers, distribution and motions of the stars in the galactic system which would make a collision, or even a close approach of a pair of stars, such a rare event in the history of the Universe that it could not possibly account for the large number of novae observed in the last hundred years. It should be added, however, that several authorities are disposed to favour the collision theory so far as the super-novae are concerned.

A second suggestion postulated the rapid entry of a star into a dense interstellar cloud with consequences very much of the same sort, but on a vaster scale, as we can observe almost nightly when a " shooting-star " or meteor streaks across the sky in a brilliant trail of light. The meteor which may be no larger than a grain of sand enters our atmosphere with a speed of 20 to 40 miles per second and as a result of the resistance of the air to this rapid motion the small body is heated to such an extent

XI. Great Nebula in Orion
(*Mt. Wilson Observatory*)

XII(a). Coal Sack and Southern Cross (Franklin-Adams)

XII(b). Double Cluster in Perseus (I. Roberts)

that it is vaporised and, becoming luminous, provides us with the well-known spectacle. In much the same way, it was urged, could the immense increase of luminosity of a nova be explained. Although, as we have seen, Nova Persei (1901)—and one other nova—is known to be associated with a nebular cloud, the explanation breaks down in the case of all the other novae that have been adequately observed.

A third theory of nova-outburst was put forward by Professor E. A. Milne a few years ago. A stable star, such as the sun, is in balance at any level in its interior under the outward pressure of the gas, of which it is composed, and of radiation pressure, against both of which is acting the weight of the layers of the star above this level. Milne showed that there were theoretical reasons for the possibility of the sudden collapse of a star, whereupon vast quantities of energy would be released resulting in the rapid expulsion of the outer stellar layers observed eventually as the expanding shell.

Since those days, we have become familiar with the new ideas relating to the method by which a star such as the Sun, for example, maintains its outpouring of heat and light by tapping the hidden energy of the atom through the process of converting hydrogen into helium in the deep recesses of the star—or, in the case of other types of stars, by processes of a similar nature. Perhaps a nova outburst can be explained in terms of the sudden transition of one process to a second of explosive tendency under conditions favourable for the emergence of the observed phenomenon. But it seems clear at the moment that there is a great deal more to learn about the details of a nova's rise to grandeur before we can do more than speculate about the mysterious processes that give birth to one of the most spectacular events in the heavens.

There is just one more matter to which we can make a brief allusion here before taking leave of novae, and that is the fate of the expanding shells. We have already remarked that the material of the shells is dissipated into interstellar space and this fact can be established in several ways.

First, the rate of expansion of a nova shell such as that of Nova Aquila (1918) showed no sign of diminishing during the years the shell was under observation; thus it may be inferred that there is little likelihood of the material of the shell falling back eventually on to the star as a result of the latter's gravitational attraction.

Second, the observed rate of expansion at or near maximum light—just when the shell is separated from the star—greatly exceeds "the velocity of escape" from the star. In the case of the Sun we can calculate from the known mass and dimensions of our luminary the value of the velocity of escape from the influence of the Sun; it is about 380 miles per second, that is to say, if an atom is shot vertically upwards from the solar surface with a speed exceeding that just mentioned the atom, if not interfered with by other atoms in its progress, will escape into space without the slightest expectation of returning to its parent body. If the speed of the atom is less than 380 miles per second, the atom will rise above the solar surface but never far enough to remove itself beyond the power of the Sun's gravitational attraction; it will eventually begin to fall towards the Sun, later to join its fellows in the solar atmosphere.

Most solar prominences are shot out above the higher levels of the Sun with speeds insufficient to carry them into space and they are seen to fall back on the Sun in mighty cascades. Occasionally a solar eruption is of such magnitude that the Sun is unable to retard sufficiently the outward-rushing streams which eventually are scattered into interplanetary regions. On more frequent occasions streams of electrons are shot out from the Sun with effects observable as so-called magnetic storms, a radio fade-out or a brilliant auroral display. In the case of novae, we can make only a rough guess as to the velocity of escape but there is little doubt that the rate of expansion of the nova-shell exceeds the velocity of escape by a very substantial margin. Accordingly, the bright novae—and the super-novae even more so—pour into interstellar space a considerable quantity of matter (in mass, however, only a minute fraction of the parent stars) and any preconceived idea that the spaces between the stars are empty must be drastically revised. In the final chapter we pursue this topic in considerably greater detail.

Chapter VIII

DELTA ORIONIS AND THE INTERSTELLAR CLOUD

In previous chapters we have been almost entirely concerned with stars and stellar systems; in this concluding chapter our attention will be mainly directed—in the first instance, at least—to the regions of space between the stars. Until comparatively recently such regions, so immense compared with the dimensions of the stars, were supposed to be entirely void of substance except for the diffuse nebulae which appeared to be somewhat compact aggregations of matter no doubt of a very tenuous density. In more recent times it was recognised that charged particles were shot out of the Sun, some of which on reaching our atmosphere were responsible for, amongst other things, the spectacular displays of the aurora borealis; further, as we have seen in the previous chapter, the expanding shells of novae were eventually dissipated into interstellar space. From such considerations it became evident that space could no longer be described as having the characteristics of a vacuum, although the total amount of matter dispersed in this way through the Galaxy, for example, was regarded as almost insignificant in comparison with the sum-total of stellar mass. We shall see in due course how this idea had to be considerably modified.

The brightly diffuse nebulae are, spectroscopically, of two kinds although, as regards material constitution, they are probably very much alike, and similar, too, to the dark or non-luminous nebulae to which we refer later in greater detail. The fact that a nebula is luminous does not necessarily mean that its brightness is a consequence, so to speak, of its own efforts, as, for example, in the case of a star which needs no outside aid to convert it into a luminous body. In the third decade of the present century Hubble, at Mount Wilson Observatory, established the eventual source of luminosity of the bright diffuse nebulae as bright stars in their immediate neighbourhood and he found that the nature of the light proceeding from the nebulae depended on the nature of the radiation emitted from the stars concerned or, in simpler terms, on their surface-temperatures. If the surface-temperature was less than 18,000° (this temperature corresponding to the hot stars of B type) the spectrum of the nebular light was similar to that of the bright star associated with the nebula. If the surface-temperature of the star in the vicinity of the nebula exceeded 18,000°, the spectrum of the nebular light bore no resemblance to that of the star and, in fact, showed the main features of the spectra of some of the planetary nebulae and of the expanding shells of novae at some considerable time after the outburst.

In the first type of luminous nebulae the brightness of the nebula is inferred to be the result of the reflection of the light from the neighbouring star by small particles. A well-known example is the nebulosity shown up in long-exposure photographs of the familiar cluster of the Pleiades, the brightest stars of which are visible to the naked eye on a clear night ; in a small telescope perhaps two or three hundred stars are seen but when a long exposure is made with a photographic telescope, the brighter stars are observed to be surrounded with great expanses of luminous clouds, the light of which is derived from the reflection of the stellar light by the constituent particles of the clouds (see Plate X (a), facing page 177).

In the second type of luminous nebula, such as the Orion nebula (Plate XI, facing page 192), the spectrum is a bright line spectrum in which hydrogen and oxygen and nitrogen lines are conspicuous—these lines must originate in the atoms of these elements, stimulated by the powerful radiation of the associated star. Amongst the bright lines are the characteristic green lines of so-called nebulium which, we have seen, are due mainly to ionised oxygen and nitrogen in a highly rarefied condition. The intensity of the ultra-violet radiation falling on hydrogen atoms, for example, is sufficient to ionise these atoms, that is, to reduce them to bare nuclei (protons) ; electrons torn from the atoms are then rushing about in all directions and occasionally, when the circumstances are favourable, a nucleus succeeds in capturing an electron which will then find itself in one of the permitted orbits (see page 80). But no sooner has the capture been effected than the electron "jumps" to an inner orbit of lesser energy, the shedding of energy taking the form of radiation. By a succession of "jumps" the electron may reach the innermost orbits and, in the process, light of the familiar wave-lengths in the visible region of the spectrum and in other wave-lengths is emitted, thus giving rise in particular to the bright lines observed in the spectrum of the nebula.

The reconstituted atom is ready to be acted upon again by the ultra-violet radiation of the star; the subsequent ionisation is followed sooner or later by the capture of a wandering electron and the process of radiation in characteristic wave-lengths then occurs once more as described. When all the circumstances are taken into account (some of them of a nature rather difficult to explain) it is inferred that the gaseous constituents of the nebula are of an almost incredibly low density, of the same degree as that of the matter in a planetary nebula or in the expanding shell of a nova.

It would be unreasonable to suppose that the two types of bright nebulae are markedly different in material constitution simply because of the fortuitous presence in their neighbourhood of one or other type of stars. We must accordingly conclude that the bright diffuse nebulae, whatever the source of their luminosity, are mainly, if not entirely, composed of free atoms of the elements—and, as we shall see later, of simple molecular compounds—and of minute particles, much smaller than grains of sand, to which it is convenient to refer as *cosmic dust*, the latter being responsible mainly for the reflection effects.

A feature of the Milky Way regions is the occurrence of dark patches void of stars. When Sir William Herschel observed one of these for the first time, his astonishment was great—a "hole in the heavens" was how he described it, a vast tunnel, as it were, in which no stellar light was visible. These patches are now known as "dark nebulae", vast obscuring clouds of the same character as the clouds forming the bright diffuse nebulae and frequently occurring in the neighbourhood of the latter. Perhaps the best known example is the "Coal Sack" (Plate XII (a), facing page 193) in the southern Milky Way, so called by the early navigators; the Coal Sack is pear-shaped, 8° in length and about 5° at its broadest. It has been found by statistical methods, taking into account the number and magnitudes of the few stars between us and the cloud, that this obscuring nebula is about 300 light-years distant; in its greatest extension at right angles to the line of sight it is about 40 light-years long. Despite its vast dimensions the Coal Sack does not succeed in obscuring entirely the light of the stars beyond, for long-exposure photographs show the dark area to be studded with faint images; it is estimated that, at its densest parts, the dark nebula cuts down the light of the stars, on the side remote from us, in varying degree by two to three magnitudes.

An example of the combination of a dark nebula with a bright nebula is shown in Plate XIII (facing page 208), the famous "horse-head" nebula in Orion. Here we have an extensive cloud covering the right half of the plate; note the silver lining, evidence of illumination by a bright star embedded within it, the "horse-head" itself being evidently a dense knot of obscuring matter not subject to the influence of the bright star. The nebula appears to have a sharp boundary, for the left hand side of the plate is studded with stars in numbers comparable with adjacent unobscured regions.

The presence of obscuring matter in Milky Way regions is often revealed by what is known as the "reddening" of distant stars. We have frequently referred to the correlation between the colours of the stars and their surface-temperatures, a red star being associated with a low temperature and a blue star with a high temperature. The assignment of colour is simply another way of stating that the maximum intensity of the continuous or rainbow spectrum occurs in the region of a particular colour, this colour predominating over all others. Again, the nature of the absorption spectrum of a star is associated with the surface-temperature; the spectrum of a cool red star, it will be recollected, shows the absorption bands of several chemical compounds and the absorption lines of many of the familiar elements, while at the other extremity of the spectral range the temperature is so high that the lines of normal (that is, complete) atoms no longer appear, since the atoms are ionised at the high temperature prevailing. Briefly, then, the predominant colour in the continuous spectrum specifies the colour of the star, and the character of the absorption spectrum gives a further clue to the surface-temperature;

in particular, a hot star (of spectral type B, say) is blue under normal circumstances.

What appears at first sight as an observational anomaly is the phenomenon of hot B type stars with a reddish colour. These stars, it should be noted, are generally at considerable distances from us. The anomaly in question is attributed to the effect of cosmic matter lying between us and the stars, not necessarily on the scale of the vast clouds with which the bright diffuse nebulae and the dark nebulae are associated. It is

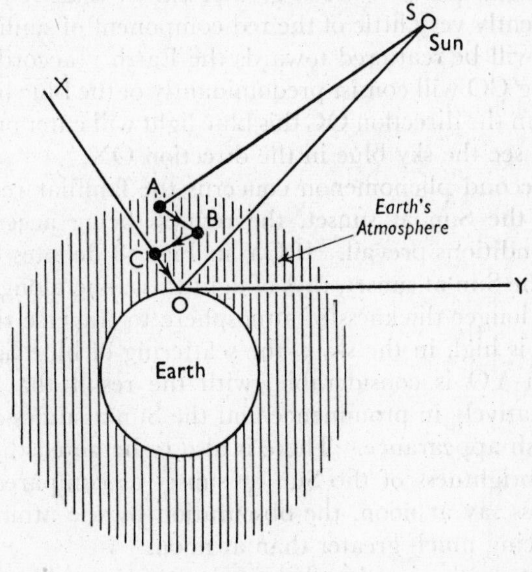

FIG. 58

evident that, if the visible radiation of a star is predominantly blue on emission from the stellar surface and predominantly red after its passage through interstellar space, then the blue light must be abstracted in some way or other from the original beam of light from the star. Familiar phenomena associated with the Sun enable us to interpret what occurs in interstellar space.

The first phenomenon is the " blueness " of the sky on a cloudless day with the Sun high in the heavens. The Earth is, of course, surrounded by an atmosphere and if we neglect, for simplicity, the refraction of a ray of light as it passes through the atmosphere, an observer at O (Fig. 58) will see the Sun in the direction given by the straight line OS. But sunlight is falling on the atmospheric shell and a ray of light such as SA will, on encountering a molecule, say, of oxygen at A be deviated into some such direction as AB and, if it encounters further molecules at B and C, may finally be deflected along CO. This deviation of rays of light by molecules is known as "scattering". Now the laws of scattering tell us that blue light is deflected to a much greater extent than red light and consequently very little of the red component of sunlight in the ray SA will be scattered towards the Earth ; accordingly, the ray along CO will consist predominantly of the blue light and if we look in the direction OC this blue light will enter our eye and we shall see the sky blue in the direction OX.

The second phenomenon concerns the familiar red appearance of the Sun at sunset, the redness being accentuated if foggy conditions prevail. If OY in Fig. 58 denotes the direction of the Sun at sunset, rays of light travelling along YO have a much longer thickness of atmosphere to traverse than when the Sun is high in the sky ; the scattering of blue light in the direction YO is considerable, with the result that red light gains relatively in prominence and the Sun assumes an orange or reddish appearance. There is also to be noted the diminution in brightness of the Sun at sunset as compared with its brightness say at noon, the obscuration by the atmosphere at sunset being much greater than at noon.

We return now to the phenomenon of the reddening of hot stars. If the star is immersed in an immense cloud such as a dark nebula of the kind previously considered, the obscuration and the scattering of blue light may be due to the gaseous constituents of the cloud or to small particles (cosmic dust) or to both. But, in regions of the Milky Way in which there is no direct evidence of obscuring matter, the reddening of a distant B type star must mean that in the long path traversed by the rays of light from the star to us there must be interstellar matter, of incredibly low density, which scatters starlight. Now, it is known that matter consisting only of atoms or molecules is a much more efficient agent of scattering than the minute particles of cosmic dust; and the examination of the spectra of the reddish B type stars seems to be conclusive that the phenomenon of reddening must be attributed mainly to the cosmic dust particles, estimated to be of diameters between a thousandth and a hundred-thousandth of an inch, and consequently that the amount of free atoms and molecules is relatively small. Recent studies have gone some way to discriminate between the two possibilities that these particles are metallic or non-metallic in character. In the case of a metallic particle only a small proportion of the light is reflected from its surface, the remainder being absorbed and converted into heat; whereas a non-metallic particle reflects most of the light falling upon it. With these principles as a guide it is inferred that the interstellar dust consists chiefly of non-metallic matter, its actual constitution being otherwise unknown.

We now turn our attention to the star which in the first place provided definite evidence of the existence of the interstellar cloud—apart from the vast bright diffuse nebulae we have been considering earlier—and in the second place specified definitely one particular constituent of the cloud. In 1904 Hartmann obtained spectra of the star Delta Orionis (see Fig. 18). This star is actually an eclipsing binary with a period of $5\frac{3}{4}$ days so that the line of sight is nearly in the plane of the orbit of one of the components about the other, or—expressed in another way—of the orbit of each component about the centre of mass of the system.

For convenience of explanation we shall suppose that the radial velocity of the centre of mass is zero. If we call the components A and B, then during part of the orbital period the radial velocity of A is one of approach while the radial velocity of B is one of recession; during the remainder of the orbital period the character of the respective radial velocities of A and B is interchanged. While the component A is moving towards us the absorption lines produced by A will be displaced from their normal positions towards the violet end of the spectrum, and while A is moving away from us the absorption lines will be displaced towards the red end of the spectrum; accordingly, during the orbital period a particular absorption line will be observed to oscillate about the position associated with its characteristic wave-length. The circumstances are precisely those we have illustrated in Fig. 42 (*a*) and (*b*), page 108. But Hartmann noticed that this particular feature did not apply to the K line associated with singly-ionised calcium atoms, for the wave-length of this line remained invariable at all times ; such a line is generally referred to as a *stationary line* to distinguish it from the oscillating lines arising from the changing radial velocities of, say, component A. Clearly, the calcium atoms could not be in either component of the binary for, if they were, the absorption lines characteristic of these atoms would be expected to partake of the oscillatory motion characteristic of the other absorption lines.

In 1909 Dr. V. M. Slipher suggested that the K line was produced by the absorption of calcium atoms lying between us and the star, but for many years this suggestion was disregarded in favour of an explanation in terms of a kind of halo of atoms surrounding the binary but not sharing in the orbital motion of either component. There can be no doubt that Slipher's explanation is the correct one. It may be added that the other prominent line—the H line—of singly ionised calcium is also found to be stationary.

The reader may be rather puzzled about the fact that the calcium atoms responsible for the stationary absorption lines are singly-ionised and are not the neutral atoms with their full complement of planetary electrons. The stars such as Delta Orionis with which the stationary lines are associated are hot B type stars ; the ultra-violet radiation from these stars easily ionises any calcium atom in its path, the expelled electron being dispatched on a solitary journey with little immediate expectation of being captured by a disrupted atom ; the ionised calcium atom has then plenty of time to absorb the quantum of energy of the correct amount from either or both components of the binary star, thereby imprinting the H and K lines in the stellar spectrum.

More recently the stationary lines of other elements have been found in stars similar to Delta Orionis ; these elements are sodium, potassium, titanium and iron. Further, in the same way, molecules of cyanogen and of a simple compound of carbon and hydrogen have been detected in interstellar space. Considering the difficulty of obtaining evidence of interstellar elements—for the density is very minute and so to obtain a detectable stationary absorption line the length of the column of gas which the light of the star traverses must be very great—it would appear to be reasonable to suggest that many more elements (if not all the usual terrestrial ones) are represented in the interstellar cloud.

In several instances a single stationary line of one or more elements is found doubled and sometimes trebled ; the inference in such cases is that one section of the column of interstellar gas has a space-velocity differing from that of the other section or sections. Further, there is evidence that in one of such sections an element such as sodium may be well represented, while in another section sodium is in such meagre supply that it is ineffective to produce even the faintest absorption lines.

The stationary lines are invariably sharp and their intensity generally increases with the distances (when known) of the stars concerned ; if we accept as a working hypothesis that in interstellar space, particularly in the Milky Way regions, the atoms of calcium, for example, are distributed with rough uniformity, then we can see how the measurement of the intensity of interstellar lines provides a new method of estimating the distances of remote stars. This method has been applied with fair success in the case of very distant objects such as novae, although it is only fair to add that, when several of such estimates of distance are checked against results obtained by other methods, the complete reliability of the hypothesis underlying the line-intensity method—as to uniform distribution of calcium atoms, say, in the interstellar cloud—is sometimes open to question.

Further evidence of the obscuring effect of interstellar matter (unconnected with the great diffuse nebulae we described earlier in the chapter) was provided by Dr. R. Trumpler's studies of " open clusters ". An open cluster, such as is shown in Plate XII (b), facing page 193, is a comparatively compact aggregation of several hundred stars, perhaps a few thousand light-years away ; such clusters, it may be added, are found only in, or close to, the Milky Way. One of the observable features of an open cluster, derivable from long-exposure photographs, is the extent of the sky which it covers or, expressed differently, its angular diameter. Now, the spectra of the brightest stars in the cluster can be obtained ; suppose, for example, several of these stars are of B-type ; their absolute magnitudes are known from the statistics enshrined in the Hertzsprung-Russell diagram and, since their apparent magnitudes are easily derivable by one of the routine observational methods, the distances of these stars and, consequently, the distance of the cluster, can be readily obtained. Combining the value of the distance with that of the angular diameter we can then derive the linear diameter (in light-years) of the cluster.

Suppose now, for simplicity, that all the open clusters are identical in linear dimensions ; from what has been said we should deduce that a cluster 1000 light-years away would appear to have twice the angular diameter of a cluster 2000 light-years away, thrice the angular diameter of a cluster 3000 light-years away, and so on. When the details of the clusters were compared, this kind of relation was found to be wholly lacking and the only way to reconcile the several observational facts was to suppose that the distances of the remoter clusters had been exaggerated owing to the apparent magnitudes of the stars being measured as too faint ; in other words, the existence of an absorbing cloud had to be postulated in order to make the whole corpus of observations consistent.

Trumpler was led to deduce that the absorbing cloud formed a layer about the galactic plane nearly 600 light-years thick and that the absorbing properties of the cloud could be specified by saying that any star in a cluster at a distance of 3000 light-years would be photographed about two-thirds of a magnitude fainter than it would have been if the galactic regions were free of interstellar matter. It may be added that Shapley's original estimates of the dimensions of the galactic system, based on his investigations of the globular clusters, were subsequently reduced when the existence of the absorbing cloud had been definitely demonstrated and its absorbing capacity ascertained.

The average density of the interstellar cloud—average, because density is hardly likely to be precisely uniform throughout the galactic regions—has been estimated in various ways; here, we can give the results only. First of all consider the mass of a hydrogen atom; it is known from physical investigations that we should require a million million million million hydrogen atoms to give us a mass of $1\frac{2}{3}$ grams. The density of the interstellar cloud is such that within a volume of a cubic inch we should expect to find only 27 hydrogen atoms if the cloud is entirely composed of hydrogen, or alternatively only one aluminium atom if the cloud is composed of aluminium atoms alone. It would then seem that, whatever the composition of the interstellar cloud may be, a cubic inch of the cloud, on the average, is hardly likely to muster more than one or two atoms.

When we think of the almost incredibly small mass of an atom it might seem that our further interest in the interstellar cloud—other than that relating to its absorbing effect—is out of all proportion to its tenuity; but when we reflect on the immense distances between the stars in the Galaxy we arrive at a different conception as to how matter is distributed. Suppose that we carve out a volume of galactic space in the shape of a sphere with a radius of 16 light-years; it is then found that the amount of interstellar matter is equivalent to the mass of 17 suns. Now we know fairly accurately from the measurements of stellar distances the number of stars within a distance of, say, 16 light-years of the Sun; according to Dr. G. P. Kuiper, the number is 48. If we regard this particular result as typifying the density of the stellar population as a whole, then it transpires—perhaps, rather surprisingly—that the interstellar cloud makes a substantial contribution to the total amount of matter in the galactic regions.

In subsequent pages we shall be concerned with the phenomenon of *galactic rotation* in which dynamical principles are involved; it is not, perhaps, difficult to see that the interstellar cloud plays a part comparable with that played by the stars. We shall first give an account of galactic rotation, paying some attention, in due course, to the confirmation of the phenomenon provided by spectroscopic observations relating to the interstellar material.

We have already remarked in a previous chapter that Halley's discovery, in 1718, of the proper motions of three prominent stars paved the way for a complete transformation of the conception of the stellar universe from one in which the stars had been previously regarded as static to one in which they were now regarded as in motion—not like ships at anchor, but like ships sailing the broad oceans in all sorts of directions and with all sorts of speeds. For nearly two centuries the only hypothesis that held the field, and was supposed to be not inconsistent with observations, was this hypothesis of the random motions of the stellar population ; the stellar universe was, in fact, regarded as a chaos. Stated more specifically in terms of our analogy, the hypothesis meant simply this that, if we concentrate our attention on all the ships in the Atlantic with speeds between 8 and 9 knots, the number of such ships steaming in a particular direction would be the same as the number steaming in any other direction. It is to be remembered, of course, that in the nautical analogy, we are making our observations from a particular ship which itself is steaming, say, north-west with a speed of 4 knots ; but this need not detain us as the effect of the ship's motion—or the solar motion in the case of the stars (see page 65)—can be ascertained and allowed for when all the necessary observational material is available.

There is another point about the definition of random motions which we may mention here, and which, of course, is adequately represented in any investigation ; just as the group of ships with speeds between, say, 30 and 31 knots is much less numerically than the group with speeds between 8 and 9 knots, so in the stellar problem our definition takes charge of a like distribution expressed in terms of a mathematical formula which we need not particularise.

In 1904 J. C. Kapteyn discovered that this particular idea of random motions conflicted with the observations of proper motions which had, by the beginning of the century, become sufficiently numerous and accurate as to be capable of precise statistical treatment. Careful analysis showed him that the motions of the stars could be expressed in terms of a somewhat more complicated phenomenon, that of the *two star-streams*, as it is called. Consider now our analogy of shipping in the

Atlantic. We suppose, for simplicity, first that all the ships in the Atlantic can be divided into two groups, one group flying the red ensign and the other group flying the stars and stripes, and second that the motions in each group have the characteristics of randomness already described. Suppose further that a constant current, setting due west at two knots, affects the ships in the first group alone ; we can then say that this group, as a whole, is moving due west at two knots. In a similar way we can imagine the second group, as a whole, to be moving due east with a speed of three knots, say. The introduction of different currents for the two groups of ships is, of course, an artificiality from the oceanographer's point of view, but perhaps the analogy may help the reader to visualise the phenomenon of the two star-streams.

In the case of the stars our observations are complicated by the fact that these are, effectively, made with reference to the Sun which is itself in motion ; however, when the effects of the solar motion are removed from the observations the characteristics of the stellar motions bear some resemblance to the Atlantic shipping in the way just described. Just as individual ships in each of the two groups may be anywhere in the Atlantic at a given moment, so in the stellar case the two groups —or streams—of stars are intermingled in space. Some years later Schwarzschild introduced an alternative way of regarding the main features of the Atlantic shipping which, in mathematical applications, is sometimes superior to Kapteyn's conception ; but as the two ways of looking at the problem lead to almost identical results in practice we need not consider Schwarzschild's theory any further.

It is to be emphasised that the two-streams theory was concerned with the stars of the galactic system and, at first, with only those in the immediate neighbourhood of the Sun—say, within 300 light-years ; as knowledge of proper motions of the fainter and still more distant stars increased in volume, the theory of star-streaming obtained additional confirmation. We can no longer think of the stars as moving in a haphazard way, but as having their motions governed by some general principle ; there is, in fact, evidence of dynamical organisation within the bounds of the galactic system the nature of which became more explicit through investigations by Professor B. Lindblad of Stockholm and Professor J. H. Oort of Leiden round about 1927. Briefly, the theory that the galactic system was rotating came into being and, being duly tested in several ways, has now become throughly established.

It is well to define more precisely what is meant by galactic rotation. The effect of the rotation of the Earth about its axis is seen daily in the apparent motions of the Sun and stars from east to west ; the explanation of this phenomenon taxed the ingenuity of the ancient Greeks to the utmost without success ; it was only when Copernicus attacked the problem of the motions of the bodies in the solar system from a new angle that a single solution depending on the hypothesis of the spinning of the nearly spherical Earth about an axis was found. Later, in Galileo's time, the apparent motion of sunspots across the solar disc suggested that the Sun was also rotating about an axis. Again, most of the planets have been found to be rotating and within comparatively recent years spectroscopic observations have made it clear that many of the stars are in rapid rotation. In each of these cases the rotation resembles—with minor reservations—the spinning of a solid fly-wheel about its axis.

Galactic rotation is different from the terrestrial rotation, for example ; strictly the term is a misnomer, being akin actually to the movements of revolution of the planets around the Sun. We mean, then, by galactic rotation the orbital motions—all described in the same direction—of the stars around what is, almost certainly, a massive concentration of stars at the centre of the Galaxy. In the planetary system the Sun is the prime controlling body. In the galactic system the dense nucleus of stars to which we have just referred acts, in the same way, as a centre of gravitational attraction. But this is not all, for the diffuse interstellar cloud and the remaining galactic stars have their own contribution to make as regards the gravitational control of a star, as the latter wends its way along its vast path around the galactic centre. The problem of investigating the stellar orbits is evidently more complex than in the planetary case ; but, nevertheless, as we shall see later, much reliable information about the details pertaining to galactic rotation has become available through recent researches.

XIII. The Horse-head Nebula in Orion
(*Mt. Wilson Observatory*)

XIV. Spiral Nebula in Canes Venatici
(Mt. Wilson Observatory)

The rotation of a liquid or gaseous globe about an axis has one well-known consequence, namely, the assumption of a somewhat flattened shape by the body concerned, the degree of flattening increasing with the rate of rotation. The earth, for example, is slightly flattened in shape, its polar diameter being about 26 miles shorter than an equatorial diameter ; this flattening is related to the rate of rotation at a time when the liquid Earth had just cooled sufficiently to allow the formation of a solid crust. Jupiter and Saturn are conspicuously flattened ; in each case the rate of rotation is exceptionally rapid. Similarly, we should expect stellar systems to be definitely flattened ; in particular, the study of our own Galaxy as summed up in its general form illustrated in Fig. 54, page 162, reveals a flattened system shaped much like a lens. Further, spectroscopic observations of several extragalactic nebulae are conclusive in showing effects characteristic of rotation ; in the frontispiece and in Plate XIV, two nebulae are shown ; the first is a lens-shaped system, seen edge-on, much like our own Galaxy, in which rotational effects have been definitely observed, and the second is one suggestive of rotation. Conversely, we might expect a flattened system such as the Galaxy to be in a state of rotation.

We can dispose of the idea that the Galaxy may be rotating in the sense in which a solid body such as a fly-wheel is rotating ; in the latter case the distance between any two points remains constant and, if this principle is applied to the Galaxy, we should expect that the distance between any two stars—say, the Sun and Sirius—would remain constant ; in other words, the observed radial velocity of Sirius—and of any other star—would be zero. This, of course, is contrary to observation, and so we must rule out rotation in this sense.

We consider now the general principles of Oort's theory of galactic rotation, restricting ourselves to stars in the galactic plane ; we assume, for simplicity, that the orbit of any such star lies in the plane of the galactic equator. In Fig. 59 the plane of the paper represents the galactic plane, C is the centre * of the Galaxy, S is the Sun and X a star at a considerable

* This is in the direction of the dense star-clouds in Sagittarius (see Plate VI (b), facing page 129).

distance from S. First consider the group of stars in the immediate neighbourhood of the Sun—say, within 300 light-years. Each of these stars will be describing an orbit around C; Oort assumed, as a working hypothesis, that on averaging out the orbital velocities of these stars a circular motion around C resulted; this is indicated by the arrowed line SA drawn perpendicular to SC.

In the same way, the average of the orbital motions of a group of stars in the immediate neighbourhood of X was represented by a velocity—indicated by the line XB—at right angles to XC. Just as in the planetary system the orbital velocity of the Earth is greater than that of a planet more remote from the Sun, so the velocity along XB where X is nearer to C than S, is greater than the velocity along SA. It is easy to

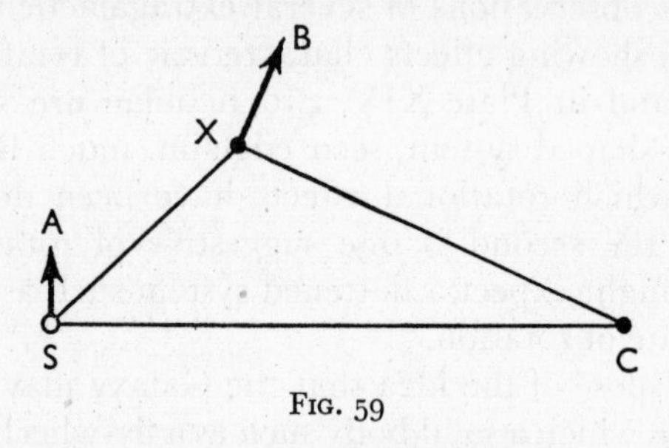

FIG. 59

see from the figure that X must be receding from S: in other words, the average radial velocity of the group of stars near X with respect to the group at S will be a velocity of recession. Further, this average velocity will be related by an explicit mathematical formula to the forces of attraction arising from the condensation of stars at C, the remaining galactic stars and the interstellar cloud.

As we can allow for the solar motion with respect to the group of stars at S, we can simplify the explanation by assuming that the Sun has a characteristic circular velocity represented by SA in Fig. 59. Accordingly, when we examine the observed radial velocities, averaged for groups of stars in different parts of the galactic plane, we should expect these to follow the mathematical relationship alluded to. Oort investigated the observed radial velocities of the distant O and B type stars grouped in the way we have described and obtained definite confirmation of the general principles of the theory. It is not too difficult to see from Fig. 59 that the motions of the stars near X will give rise to an average proper motion, as observed from the Sun, which will have characteristic properties depending on the particular location of X in the galactic plane ; despite certain difficulties in dealing with proper motions, general confirmation of the theory of galactic rotation comes from this quarter also.

We return now to the interstellar cloud and see how it contributes to the theory. We recollect that the stationary H and K lines of calcium in the spectra of distant B type stars, for example, originate in the interstellar cloud lying between us and the stars. If, as must be supposed, galactic rotation is a general phenomenon, then the cloud must share in this rotation ; accordingly, the effect of rotation must be reflected in the wave-lengths of the stationary lines.

Consider a column of calcium atoms distributed uniformly between us, at S, and a star at X (Fig. 59). The rotational velocity of these atoms will vary along the column between S and X, but the effect will be substantially the same as if all the atoms were concentrated at a point midway between S and X and revolving in a circular orbit about C. The observed radial velocities given by the displacements of the H and K lines in the spectra of the stars at or near X can then be used to test the theory, just as if these lines referred to a star midway between S and X and moving around C in a circular orbit. Now, the observed radial velocity arising from Oort's hypothesis of rotation is proportional to the distance between S and the stars concerned ; accordingly, the observed radial velocities derived from the interstellar cloud—or from the hypothetical star midway between S and X—should be half of the average radial velocity observed for the group of stars at X. We thus have a valuable check on the theory of galactic rotation. In a celebrated investigation J. S. Plaskett and J. A. Peirce examined the radial velocities arising from the interstellar cloud and those arising from the stars concerned, and in every part of the galactic regions observed they obtained complete confirmation.

At this point it may be convenient to give some indication of the relation between galactic rotation and the two-streams theory. In the latter theory it is well to remember that the observational evidence comes from stars in the immediate vicinity of the Sun—at any rate at distances small compared with the distance of the galactic centre from the Sun. In Fig. 60 consider the stars lying in a small sector of the galactic plane, bounded by the lines SA and SB, and situated near the Sun. These stars describe orbits around C, parts of which are indicated by the dotted lines. For simplicity we shall suppose that the Sun, S, is moving along ST drawn perpendicular to SC. It is, then, perhaps evident in a general way, although the full explanation would be long and difficult, that the distribu-

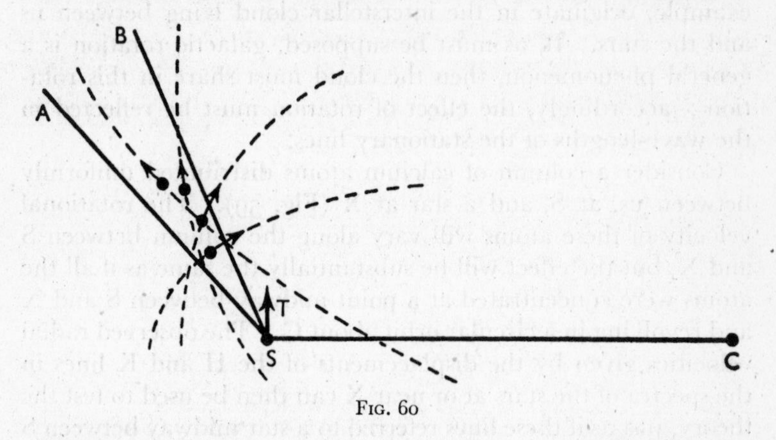

FIG. 60

tion of stellar motions suggested in Fig. 60 resembles the east-ward-bound and westward-bound groups of shipping in the Atlantic which we used as our analogy in trying to explain the two-streams theory. The ideas illustrated in the figure have been expressed in mathematical form by Lindblad.

We now come to the problem of finding out the magnitude of the average orbital velocity of the stars in the immediate neighbourhood of the Sun ; as before, for simplicity, we shall suppose that the Sun has this average orbital velocity—the velocity in a circle around the galactic centre, C, of radius equal to the distance of the Sun from C. Our object then is to find the Sun's velocity from suitable observations. We make use of the observed radial velocities of the globular clusters which, as will be recollected from Fig. 54, form a system fairly symmetrically disposed on each side of the galactic plane. It is almost certain that the system of clusters is also rotating—probably about an axis through the galactic centre and perpendicular to the galactic plane ; but so far nothing definite of this kind has been discovered, mainly because of the lack of sufficient observational material—up to the present our spectroscopic equipment has been able to deal with rather less than a third of the hundred clusters known and those the nearest. Perforce we have to omit such considerations and accordingly we regard effectively each cluster as a fixed landmark in the galactic scheme.

The problem before us is substantially the same as that of deriving the solar motion with respect to the stars in the Sun's neighbourhood. The radial velocities of the clusters observed give us the result that the Sun is moving with a speed of about 180 miles per second in a direction nearly at right angles to the line joining the Sun to the galactic centre, in qualitative agreement with the theory of galactic rotation. It need hardly be said that this is a department of observational astronomy where more data are urgently required for a more complete and accurate understanding of galactic dynamics ; in particular, it is eminently desirable that the general nature of the motions of the clusters as a whole should be ascertained with some exactitude, for such motions must have an effect on the quoted value of the Sun's orbital velocity around the galactic centre which has been derived on the simple hypothesis that the clusters are stationary.

Meanwhile, we can make one or two interesting deductions from the value of orbital velocity just derived. With a speed of 180 miles per second the time required by the Sun to make a complete circuit of the Galaxy—corresponding to the time required by a planet to describe its orbit around the Sun—is easily found to be, in round figures, 200 million years. Again, since the balance of informed opinion appears to favour an age for the Galaxy of about three or four thousand million years it follows that the Sun cannot have made more than a score of circuits of the Galaxy.

Oort's investigation of the phenomenon of galactic rotation

leads to an estimate of the total mass of the Galaxy, to which we have already referred (page 163). It is to be remembered that the theory involves an assumption as to the nature of the attracting forces acting, say, on the Sun. The implications of the theory are then confronted with observations and certain numerical results emerge. There is first, the mass of the condensation of stars around the galactic centre which is found to be equivalent to about one-eighth of a billion solar masses, and, second, the mass of the remaining stars together with the cosmic cloud which is found to be just about half of the mass quoted for the galactic nucleus. Adding these together, we find that the total mass of the Galaxy is equivalent, approximately, to

200,000 million solar masses.

These results may not inspire complete confidence as to their essential accuracy, owing to the comparative paucity of available material of the special kind required ; but it would be somewhat rash to suggest that they are anything but of the right order of magnitude. No doubt, when more observations accumulate—especially of the galactic clusters—we shall be able to derive an estimate of the total galactic mass which will carry conviction in all quarters.

We have seen that the mass of the interstellar cloud is comparable with the mass of the stars in the Galaxy—some astronomers go so far as to say that the total galactic mass is equally divided between cloud and stars—and several questions naturally arise. We may ask if the diffuse matter of galactic space has existed, substantially as it is at present, since the Galaxy came into being, or if, on the contrary, it is the stuff of which the stars are born or if, again, it is being constantly increased significantly in quantity by the expulsion of matter from the stars themselves. In the present state of astronomical science there seem to be no final answers to these questions. We know, of course, that matter is ejected from novae and even from such a staid star as the Sun ; on the other hand, as the stars wend their way through galactic space, they will tend to sweep up the cloud lying in their paths. Again, the more conspicuous masses of diffuse matter such as the Pleiades and Orion nebulae may, through gravitational attraction, condense into stars. Here we find ourselves in the interesting field of cosmic speculation with no sure clue yet to lead us to a fuller understanding of the evolution of the Galaxy. When Hartmann first observed the stationary calcium lines in the spectrum of Delta Orionis he had no inkling of the vista opened up by his discovery. So, too, we may be on the threshold of new developments which will bring a fuller enlightenment of the processes of nature in celestial realms.

INDEX

(The numbers refer to the pages)